Five Days in Istanbul

Maisie Sullivan

A CIP catalogue record for this book is available from The British Library.

ISBN 978-1-7398775-0-7

Printed by Amazon UK

For my boys

You all, always, encouraged me to do
it - now I have.

Acknowledgements

With thanks to:

The one and only Michael Heppell, without whose knowledge, encouragement and support this would not have been possible.

Anne Anderson for being a phenomenal alpha reader, beta reader and proofreader.

Members of Write that Book Masterclass Summer 2021 for their support, encouragement and guidance.

My #focus group whose support has been invaluable.

My Wednesday Girls…for so much!

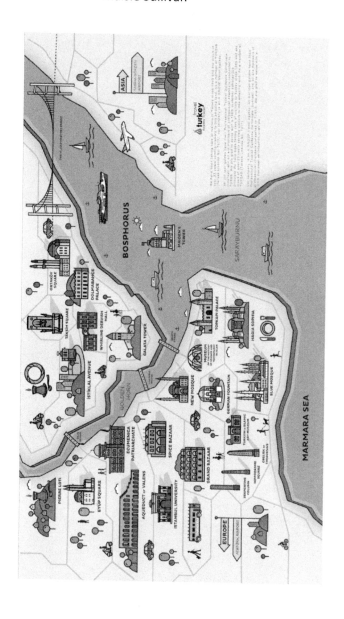

Chapter 1

The Background

What do three, forty-something, ex-pat friends, living and working in the United Arab Emirates, have in common? They are married, are teachers and they have three words that can sometimes fill them with dread. 'Mummy!' 'Miss!' and Expectations! With eight children, age five to mid-teens between them, and responsibility for another 300 or more, you can see how their time and patience might be stretched.

Theirs has been a long friendship, although some might think it a little strange. The casual observer would probably think they didn't even like one another, as they enjoy nothing more than baiting each other with sarcastic barbs and practical jokes when left to their own devices.

Ann has a very dry sense of humour, likes things to be 'ordered' so she can feel in control, but can be a little bit 'schoolmarmish' at times. Marriage to Reza (who is the complete opposite) can be challenging.

Ruth, married to Toufiq, is so laid back she's almost horizontal. Wafting her way through life and admitting to living, for the most part, on 'planet Zog.'

Abi allows her husband Mitri to think he is in control. She has a mischievous side, is adept at hiding her emotions, and doesn't take herself, or anyone else, too seriously.

They enjoy a comfortable, but not extravagant, lifestyle. Taking advantage of and experiencing all the benefits that the region has to offer. Beaches, mountains, deserts…and shopping malls *(lots of shopping malls)*. But these benefits also come with responsibilities.

As teachers, they have many responsibilities during school hours, that often continue when the school day ends. Then they have the usual stuff mums everywhere have to juggle.

The expectations of the local ex-pat community to *'join in'* puts additional pressure on them. If they're not ferrying their own and other people's kids around to various clubs and interests, they feel obligated to attend meet-ups at the local ex-pats club. Usually, at least one of the days at the weekend involves trips to shopping malls. Which are very lavish, very big, and very crowded. But they are places that are safe enough to allow the children to go off together as a group. Leaving the three friends to grab a brief moment of adult space.

You may find them sitting in a hotel foyer somewhere, sipping coffee, waiting to pick up the kids from another birthday party. *(There are **lots** of birthday parties too)*. Sometimes, they head to the beaches of Jumeirah or Jebal Ali for the day. Or, occasionally, they get to spend family weekends at the Beach Hotel in Khor Fakkan.

Some would think this an idyllic lifestyle – but it can also be physically and mentally draining. They long for a little 'me' time, to let their hair down, do grown-up, adult stuff, and just be Ann, Ruth, and Abi!

Yet another of those birthday parties, in January 1999, was the straw that finally broke the camel's back.

Chapter 2

Rebellion

Ann was constantly tapping her fingers on the table with her left hand, the knuckles of her right hand beginning to turn white, as she gripped the handle of her cup. *For god's sake!* They'd only been there about ten minutes and already the noise was becoming deafening. Shouting, screeching, and screaming filled the air; the boom of the bass echoing around the foyer as yet another of the, seemingly endless, kids' birthday parties got into full swing.

'I need to get out of here,' she said, to nobody in particular, but almost immediately Ruth responded with 'Yep, I'm with you – let's go now before I turn rogue.'

'Don't you think we ought to wait, if only to make sure the kids are ok?' Abi appeared hesitant.

'Do you want me to end up in jail?' Ann slammed her cup on the table. 'If I don't escape this racket - *like now* - I will definitely do someone some damage. For god's sake. All you need to do is go and tell them we'll pick them up later. They'll be fine with Julie.'

Ruth grabbed her jacket, jumped up, and headed for the door. 'You two coming then or what?'

Ann didn't need to be asked twice. Shovelling everything into her bag and scraping her chair back, she quickly followed Ruth.

Catching up with them Abi asked 'OK, where now? Shall we go to the coffee shop in the Amaris? It's usually quiet in there this time of day.'

They walked the short distance to the hotel and despite being January the evening was pleasant and warm. Ordering their drinks they decided to sit outside by the pool while they waited.

'So, what's up with you, you moody mare?' Abi asked. 'Who's rattled your cage tonight?'

'I'll tell you what's up with me,' Ann raised her voice. 'Another weekend. Another holiday coming up. Another kid's party. You and I know that all we'll end up doing for the next couple of weeks is ferrying our own and other people's kids all over the place. It's been a hard term so far and I really, really need a break.'

The tea and coffees arrived and the three friends lapsed into silence but their trains of thought were all now on the same track. Escape.

OK,' said Abi 'We could go to Khor Fakkan for a few days next week maybe?'

'No way. You know what would happen,' said Ann.

'Yeah – we'd end up having to take all the kids with us.' said Ruth 'And there'll probably be loads of kids from school there too.'

'OK – so what do you suggest then?' asked Abi.

'I suggest we go over there.' Ruth pointed across the road at the brightly-lit travel agent's window with its flashing neon sign.

'Oh yes,' Ann followed her gaze 'let's do that.'

Crossing the road almost at a run, they entered the inner sanctum of travel and adventure.

'Good evening ladies, how may I help you?' asked the young man behind the desk. 'Please, take a seat.'

Sitting down they looked at each other, none of them too sure as to exactly what they wanted or where they wanted to go, they only knew it had to be soon, not too far to travel and within their budgets.

'We'd like to book a short trip, for maybe four or five days, not too far away but somewhere interesting and offering places to visit within easy reach of a central base. We're happy to share a room but would like a good hotel, in a safe area but at a reasonable price.' Ann piped up in her schoolmarmish voice.

'Do you have any idea of where?'

'Not really,' said Abi 'We're pretty open-minded.'

'I see. Ok, let's have a look at what is available. Is it for the three of you?'

'Yes,' was the emphatic response.

'When are you thinking of going?'

'Within the next couple of days.' said Ann.

The young man pulled his computer towards him and quickly typed in a few details, scrolling through the available trips showing on his screen.

'It appears there are some good deals for Turkey at the moment. Will you be wanting city or seascape?'

Again, they looked at each other but seemed to come to a joint decision very quickly. Considering where they lived, they were already within a ten or fifteen-minute drive to several beaches, so it didn't take a lot of thinking about.

'City.' Ann glanced towards Abi and Ruth for confirmation. Both nodded in agreement.

The young man typed in a few more details, scrolled up and down his screen, and then said, 'There is a flight to Istanbul very early on Monday morning, which would get you there for around nine o'clock, and I can get you a return flight for Friday evening, arriving back in Dubai shortly after midnight. How does that sound?'

'Perfect!' said Ann, again looking at Abi and Ruth for acceptance.

'I will place those on hold for you and we can look at hotels. You will be looking at the Fatih district, if you want to be close to the sights and shopping zones. It is a good, safe area and there are some nice four-star hotels there.'

The three friends were smiling broadly. 'That sounds wonderful.' Ruth couldn't contain her excitement.

After a few more entries he said, 'So, we have the Ayrias hotel with the availability of a triple room. Very nice hotel, Art Deco-ish style and including breakfast. We also have the Miramar with availability but that is one double and a single, also including breakfast. Also…'

'The Ayrias please,' Abi pleaded.

'I knew you were going to say that!' Ann gently pushed her. 'You and your Art Deco obsession.'

'Is that OK with you Ruth?' Abi looked at her, almost begging.

'Sounds good to me.' said Ruth

'The Ayrias then, please.' Ann began to get her purse ready for payment.

'That's all then ladies. I will confirm your flights and book your room at The Ayrias. I wish all my customers were as easy to please.'

Maybe they're not as desperate for a bit of peace and quiet, Ann thought. She did, however, feel guilty for feeling that way.

Pressing the 'enter' key with a flourish the young man confirmed everything was booked. 'The total cost for the five days, including flights and hotel comes to a total of two thousand seven hundred and twenty- two fifty.'

'Pounds?' choked Ann in horror. 'Each?'

'No, no, no madam. In dirhams and for all three. Do you want me to work it out in pounds?'

Ann exhaled loudly. 'Oh. Thank goodness for that. No, no need. We can work that out later. So I work out that's nine hundred and seven dirhams fifty each.'

'Wow, that's amazing value. Are you sure that's correct?' Ruth was sceptical.

'Yes madam, look.' He turned his screen around so they could all see the total figure showing on his computer.

'You can close your mouth now.' Ann glanced at Abi who, it appeared, was stunned into silence.

'We'd spend that and more on trips and food for ourselves and the kids over the next couple of weeks.' she finally said.

'So, you paying then?' Ruth grinned, noticing Ann already had her purse out.

'No, I'm bloody not.' Ann replied. 'Unless you want to use my card and then you two can either give me the cash or pay the money into my account tomorrow.'

'Would be easier that way, rather than faffing around paying with three different cards,' Abi suggested.

'Good job I trust you.'

'Course you can trust us. We're teachers.' Abi's purse was still in her bag.

So, less than forty-five minutes after they had entered the travel agents, they left having booked a five-day trip to Istanbul – for them only. It was going to be a blast and they only had three days to wait for take-off.

They were so excited at the prospect of five days away and the ridiculous price they had paid for the experience, they *almost* forgot to go back and pick their children up from the party.

Now all they needed to do was to go home and tell their respective partners.

They needn't have worried. Thankfully, as it was a government holiday, the three men were also on leave. Toufiq said he would take their children camping in the desert for a few days. Reza and Mitri both said they could keep their children entertained with days out.   Reza added the caveat that he wouldn't have been happy if Ruth wasn't going, as he deemed her to the '*the sensible one*'.

Chapter 3

Dubai Airport

It was approaching midnight, the air was balmy but on it wafted the distinct essence of aviation fuel from the stream of jet planes landing and taking off.

Even at this hour, Dubai International Airport was busy, crowds of people arriving, waiting to check-in, waiting for flight call announcements, or waiting for friends and relatives to appear in the arrival hall.

Ann stood just inside the door to the departures section, where she'd agreed to meet up with Ruth and Abi. The clickety-clack of suitcase wheels and the click-click of ladies in heels, assaulted her ears as they moved, some leisurely and some obviously in a last-minute panic, across the pristine marble flooring in the main terminal building. Many of the men were in their traditional white Arab dress and some of the women were in the customary black abaya (similar to a kaftan). There were also many dressed in European garb, all blending together, seamlessly, as Ann stood, watching the world go by.

The low-level background noise was reminiscent of a bee swarm.

Their flight wasn't until three forty-five a.m. but as Ann was full of nervous excitement to get started on their trip to Istanbul she'd arrived early. She'd enjoyed people watching but after about 40 minutes it became tedious and she was becoming fidgety, frequently shifting and shuffling her feet and delving into her bag for unnecessary objects.

'Hello bitch.' Abi's usual greeting.

'Hi, cow bag.' Ann's usual response. 'Where's Ruth?'

'Fannying around as usual.' laughed Abi.

'I am *NOT* fannying around. This stupid suitcase simply needs to go in a straight line – is that too much to ask of it? Is it?' Ruth was looking somewhat stressed already (unusual for her) and they weren't even at the check-in yet.

'Oooooooh, touchy.' Ann laughed.

Once Ruth had calmed down and they had located a trolley for their luggage, the three friends found their flight on the departure screens and then made their way towards the check-in area. None of them had a great deal of baggage, it was only a short break after all.

Tickets and passports were handed over. Once all checked in and boarding passes received they headed for the nearest watering hole. It was a four-and-a-half-hour flight to Istanbul and as it was a night flight, they weren't too sure what refreshments they would get on the plane. So far so good.

Relieved of their bags and free to amble aimlessly for at least another half hour, it was somewhere around this point that holiday fever began to affect Ann and Abi's behaviour. Ruth was meandering on ahead in her usual floaty, slinky fashion, lost in her thoughts and not noticing what her friends were doing. A perfect opportunity for the wind-ups to begin.

'Right, over here' said Abi, quickly disappearing behind one of the tall, wide, marble columns that adorned the duty-free area. Ann joined her and the two of them, giggling like schoolgirls, watched Ruth merrily going about her window shopping, chatting away to nobody.

It wasn't too long before Ruth realised she was on her own, suddenly noticing that she was getting no response to her chatter, she stopped and looked around. Ann and Abi were nowhere to be seen.   She wasn't actually freaking out, but from behind the column her two friends could see the look of confusion and panic begin to show on her face as she stood there, glancing this way and that.

'Let's put her out of her misery' said Ann.

'No way. Let's see how long we can 'tail' her for' said Abi.

The two of them ducked and dived amongst the columns, advertising boards and seating areas, (drawing some very suspicious looks from passers-by) keeping a close eye on their friend who seemed slightly anxious, but was at least heading towards the right boarding gate but showing all the signs of increasing stress levels.

Ann and Abi managed to get ahead of her and stepped out from behind a large billboard.

'Where've you been? We've been looking everywhere for you.' said Ann.

Unfortunately, at this point, Abi couldn't help bursting into laughter.

'You pair of bitches,' cried Ruth 'You did that on purpose.'

'As if.' said Ann – stifling a laugh.

At this point, the call *'Flight TK1958 to Istanbul now boarding at Gate 25'* came over the tannoy.

'That's us.' Ann said. So they made their way to the gate, handed over their boarding cards and passports, and boarded the plane.

Once they had settled the argument about who was going to have to sit in the middle, which Ruth lost, and Abi grabbed the window seat, they settled back for the flight. Eventually, the cabin lights were dimmed and the night flight hush soon descended. Shortly after take-off Ruth and Ann were snoozing and Abi was deeply engrossed in the book she was reading. She didn't sleep much, being a bit of an insomniac.

The flight was smooth and without incident, and a little over four hours later they were landing in Istanbul.

Chapter 4

Istanbul Airport

It was early morning as the plane descended, the lights on the runway all that were visible outside. As the plane taxied to a stop there was a round of applause from the passengers, which, apparently, was customary on this particular airline. This was quickly followed by the usual rush of people trying to grab their luggage from the overhead lockers and belongings from their seats.

'For crying out loud!' shrieked Ann, as she felt yet another jab from someone's suitcase. 'Do they think the plane will take off again before everyone's disembarked?'

'Calm down,' said Ruth 'You know this is what it's always like. We're in no hurry so let's simply chill and let the idiots off first.'

Abi had somehow managed to get her hand luggage down in lightning speed and was way ahead of them, almost out of sight and out of the door.

They managed to find her again on the shuttle bus between the plane and the terminal building, so they were all together as they entered the arrivals lounge, where the queues for immigration were already snaking around the various desks.

'Listen, give me your passports and I'll go get the visa stamps.' said Ann 'I know what to do because I was here last year with Reza. I'll pay for them and we can sort it out afterward. You two go queue up at the immigration window. At least that way we'll cut down on some of the waiting.' No-one argued. Ruth and Abi headed off to queue at passport control and Ann went off to the visa desk.

'It's strange,' thought Ann *'how I always feel nervous at this point in a journey. Like someone's going to shout "Stop!" any minute.'*

She finally got to the desk and handed over the three passports, together with the visa fees. The woman behind the counter gave them a cursory glance, stamped them, and handed them back, without issue. Ann breathed a sigh of relief.

Turning away from the desk, she decided to check what pages the visa stamps were on, thinking it would be easier at passport control. That's when she realised.

'Oh shit! No, no, no – this can't be right. She must have given me the wrong one, surely, otherwise, we wouldn't be here – would we?' Ann could feel her palms beginning to sweat.

Trying not to act suspiciously, and making every effort not to panic, she managed to find Ruth and Abi, who had crept forward in the queue. They were almost at the window with only a few people in front of them.

'OK?' asked Abi.

'Well, that depends – who has what colour passport?' asked Ann 'Mine's blue.'

'Mine's one of the red European ones.' said Abi.

'And mine's blue too.' said Ruth.

'Really?' said Ann 'So if mine's blue, Ruth's is blue and yours is red Abi, I should have two blue and one red. Yes?'

'Err yes.' said Abi.

Ann fanned the passports out in her hand. 'So how come I have two red ones and one blue one then?' she asked.

'What?' they both responded together.

Ann showed them her blue passport, handed a red one to Abi, and looked at Ruth, with alarm beginning to rise. 'This other *RED* passport – *RED NOT BLUE* – is yours, Ruth. Or is it?'

'What do you mean.' Ruth replied, 'No! That's not mine. Mine's definitely blue.'

'Maybe it is.' said Ann *'BUT THIS IS NOT YOUR PASSPORT!'* It's Jay's.' (Jay is Ruth's 8-year-old son. The passport Ann held in her hand was the one he had had since he was a BABY.)

'Don't be bloody stupid,' said Abi. 'How can it be? How did we manage to get through passport control in Dubai?'

'Good question,' exclaimed Ann.

Visibly shaking, Ruth opened the passport, hoping it was all some big mistake. Or another of Ann's wind-ups and she'd got it wrong – but nope – there was baby Jay's picture smiling back at her. She drained of all colour as Abi and Ann stared at her with a mixture of disbelief and incredulity.

'Just check your bloody bag! Perhaps you gave me the wrong one and you have your one in your bag.'

'This can't be happening,' cried Ruth. 'I know I don't have any other passport with me. I was running a bit late and grabbed it from the desk on my way out the door. It was the only one there.'

The queue had moved further forward and now there were only two couples in front of them…

'What are we going to do?' Ruth was almost sobbing now.

'Look, give Ann the passports, she can hand them over together and you stand behind us. Maybe they won't notice,' Abi said but with about as much conviction as a chocolate teapot might have if faced with a boiling kettle.

'Oh right! Put me in the bloody firing line why don't you?' Ann was not impressed at being nominated.

It was their turn at the passport control desk. A less than friendly-looking official held out his hand. Ann couldn't look him in the eyes. She was trying to appear nonchalant but her palms were clammy and her hands were trembling. She handed the passports over to him but behind her, she could sense Abi and Ruth's tension rising. Ruth was breathing quite heavily, muttering to herself and Abi was doing her 'fidgety' thing with her feet. They knew, they all knew this wasn't going to go well but it was too late now, there was not a thing they could do but wait. The immigration officer went through them, one by one, looking down at each passport and then looking up at the three of them standing there. There was a sudden change in his demeanour as he took a double-take. 'Where baby?' he asked.

'Bugger!' thought Ann. 'That's it, we've been sussed.'

As the three friends, getting increasingly worried, tried to explain the error, a very long, quite heated conversation took place. But no one was listening and the language barrier wasn't helping.

It was becoming obvious that the immigration officer either didn't understand what they were saying or simply didn't believe them. He picked up the telephone and made a call, speaking in Turkish, so none of them had a clue what was being said.

The queue behind them was becoming agitated by the delay, and inquisitive about what the hold-up was. Replacing the telephone the officer waved his hand, gesturing for them to move to one side. Making it very clear they were not to move too far.

That's when Abi noticed two rather large, stern-looking, security guards striding towards them.

'I think this is about to get a whole lot worse.' she said.

Ruth was now truly beginning to panic as one of the officers spoke to her. But of course, as none of them spoke Turkish, she simply looked at him blankly. A third official then appeared, who, speaking in English to Ann and Abi, suggested they take a seat at the side of the passport control area. She explained that Ruth was going to be taken away and questioned on suspicion of trying to enter the country illegally, but as their passports and papers were in order, they would not need to go with her.

The immigration officer made a signal, and flanking Ruth on either side, the two security guards carted her off, her Mary Poppins boots scuttling along at a rate of knots to keep up with them. She turned back and looking over her shoulder implored Ann and Abi 'Tell them I'm not a terrorist! Please – tell them I'm not a terrorist!' as she disappeared into the distance.

At this point, Ann and Abi both burst out laughing. Whether this was through fear, panic, or merely the plain irrationality at the sight of their friend disappearing from view between the two security guards, is hard to say.

'Oh my God. This is a good start isn't it,' said Ann. 'We'll probably either be on the next available plane out of here or we'll have to hang around waiting for Ruth to appear in court.'

'I simply don't get it.' said Abi 'How the hell wasn't this picked up in Dubai?'

The two sat and contemplated their friend's fate, but if truth be told, without too much consternation.

A strange man, carrying a large tray, suddenly appeared from nowhere. 'Coffee? Water? Dates?' he asked.

Realisation dawned on them that it was the first day of Eid al-Fitr, Ramadan having ended the day before, and traditionally, such things are offered first thing in the morning to enable people to break their fast. They both welcomed the light refreshments, they'd had nothing since the night before. Ann had slept most of the way and Abi was too engrossed in her book to think about food or drink.

'Every cloud' laughed Abi.

The next couple of hours seemed, to both of them, to pass in a flash. The offers of refreshments, chocolates, and food kept coming, so that, in reality, they didn't notice how long Ruth had been gone.

They talked and made up stories about the travellers and airport staff all around them. 'I know what this is,' cried Ann 'it's sonder.'

'What the hell is 'sonder'?' asked Abi.

'It's a new word I learnt – basically, it means that everyone has a story, like us and all these people.'

'You made that up! Never heard of it'

'Fine. You'll have to go look it up in the Dictionary of Obscure Sorrows,' Ann replied.

'Is that even a thing?'

'Course it is. Would I lie to you?'

'Pfft!'

And that was the end of that conversation.

Then, out of the corner of her eye, Abi had noticed Ruth re-appearing from behind one of the security guards who had carted her off earlier on.

'What time do you call this?' asked Abi, glancing at her watch. 'We've been sitting here for over two hours.'

Ruth looked as if she was going to burst into tears any second.

'Don't be nasty,' said Ann. 'Look at her. She looks scared witless.'

'She is witless,' said Abi. 'Anyone who thinks they can travel almost nineteen hundred miles on their baby's passport must be.'

Ruth shrank back in horror. 'You don't mean that. You don't know what I've been through for the last couple of hours.'

'No, I don't,' replied Abi popping another chocolate into her mouth 'but we've had a whale of a time waiting for you.'

'Okay, okay. Enough.' said 'Ruth 'Please can we get out of here now. I'll tell you all about it on the way.'

'So, they're letting you go?' It surprised Ann they were being allowed to continue their holiday.

'Yes. They've given me a seventy-two-hour visit visa and somehow I have to try and get my passport couriered from Dubai. Until I get it I have to report back here to security every morning but otherwise, I am free to go.'

'Wow! Surprising. So, they're not locking you up then?' asked Abi in a somewhat sceptical tone, with a hint of irony thrown in for good measure.

'Can we please get out of here?' pleaded Ruth.

'That question's what got us here in the first place.' chuckled Ann. At which point they all laughed and somehow managed to relax.

They found their way out of the airport to the nearest taxi rank and were soon on the way to their hotel, which they were told was around a twenty-five-minute drive.

Chapter 5

The Hotel

As the taxi pulled up outside the Ayrias Hotel, in the Fatih district of Istanbul, the three friends were feeling exhausted after their experiences so far and the fifty-five-minute journey from the airport.

'Twenty-five minutes my eye!' commented Ann.

'Oh come on. Obviously, they didn't allow for the traffic at this time of the morning,' said Ruth, surprisingly calm after her recent ordeal.

'Pfft' from Abi.

Well, this looks nice doesn't it,' said Ruth looking at the exterior of the hotel. 'It's on a main road but at least we shouldn't have any problems with taxis and stuff if we want to go anywhere.'

'Let's hope it's not going to take us fifty-five minutes to get to the airport every morning.' said Abi. 'Otherwise, we'll never get anywhere.'

Whilst this conversation was happening, the taxi driver had unloaded their bags and the hotel 'kapici', or concierge, had taken them into the foyer.

'Come on you two,' said Ann 'Let's get inside. It's bloody freezing out here.' Istanbul doesn't tend to be very balmy in January.

The warmth of the hotel foyer was most welcome to the three friends and they were as impressed with the inside of the hotel as they had been with the exterior. Very Art Deco-ish. Bold colours, clean simple lines with lots of geometric shapes. The overall feeling was one of elegance, a little faded in places but impressive and luxurious looking, nevertheless. Functional but comfortable furnishings.

'Oooh nice,' said Abi whose absolute favourite style was anything Art Deco.

As they approached the highly polished reception desk there was a group of staff talking together and giving them some strange looks.

'Good morning madam,' said one of the female staff. (Whom they later learnt was called Miray.) 'Welcome to The Ayrias Hotel. We hope you will have a pleasant stay with us. What name is your booking made in?'

Ann, again, passed over their passports but none of them could remember whose name they had made the booking in.

'Aah…' said Miray, smiling sweetly 'You are the English ladies with no passport yes?'

That certainly explained the strange looks.

'Er yes,' said Ann. 'How did you know?'

'We had a call from security at the airport to check on the validity of your booking,' said Miray – still smiling sweetly but with an added twinkle in her eye. 'We are pleased that we were able to confirm this for you.'

'Thank you,' all three said simultaneously. 'It's been quite a morning.'

'Of course. You must be tired, why don't you take a seat and I will arrange some refreshments for you before you go up to your room.'

'Why thank you very much,' said Ruth 'That would be wonderful.'

'Madam, we don't get many Ünlü here. So you are most welcome.'   (Ünlü means 'celebrities' in Turkish.)

Soaking up the atmosphere the three sat in the restaurant area and waited for their coffee and cake, but Ann had insisted on and ordered tea.

'I don't know about you two but I am so impressed with this.' said Ann 'It looks nothing like I was expecting. So much better.'

'I think I've died and gone to heaven.' said Abi 'Needs a bit of TLC in places but still my ideal surroundings.'

Ruth remained quiet, she too loved the vibe of the place but was wondering how she was going to get hold of her passport within the next couple of days. It wasn't going to be easy and Toufiq was going to be less than impressed. C'est la via! Coffee and cake first, then she would worry about it.

The three friends lapsed into silence, each with their thoughts about the journey so far and the problem of the passport.

Thankfully, the waiter brought their coffee, tea, and cake very quickly and waved away the offer of payment, which made it taste even better.

Able to relax, for the first time since they arrived, they sat and watched the comings and goings in the reception area, bar, and restaurant. Many people were finishing breakfast and others appeared to be going off out for a day's sightseeing, with their backpacks and maps at the ready.

After a while, Abi said 'I suppose we'd better go up to the room and decide what we're going to do?'

'I'm dreading phoning Toufiq. He's going to hit the roof.' said Ruth.

'Don't worry, at least he'll be doing it from a distance.' said Abi laughing 'So you won't have to peel him off the ceiling.'

They went up in the lift to the second floor and were pleasantly surprised when they entered their room to find it was not only spacious (as it was a triple room they had thought it might be a little cramped) it was furnished very much in keeping with the rest of the hotel.

'Oh wow,' said Ann, pulling her coat around her as she stepped out onto the balcony. 'Come and look at this view.'

In the near distance, they could see the imposing Fatih mosque, with its central dome and minarets dominating the skyline.

'Didn't that once used to be a church?' enquired Ann.

'No – I think it was rebuilt on the site of what used to be a church. As far as I know, the original church was in a very poor state and was demolished in the 15th century, so that the mosque could be built. The mosque itself though has also been rebuilt several times due to earthquake damage.' said Abi knowingly.

'Ooooh get you Miss Smarty Pants.' Ann raised her eyebrows.

'I only know cos I did a bit of research before we came when I knew what area we were going to be staying in.'

'Great, you'll be our gour tide then.' said Ruth.

'Gour tide?' laughed Ann 'Don't you mean tour guide?'

'No – I mean gour tide. Everything she does is arse about face so...'

As they returned to the room, with bags, coats, shoes, etc strewn around, Ruth picked up her case and placed it on the bed nearest the bathroom.

'Oh right, you're having that bed then?' asked Abi

'I'm having this one,' said Ann throwing her case onto the middle of the three beds and then promptly throwing herself onto it too. As she did so the beds parted and she fell between them and landed on the floor.

'Typical,' she laughed. ' If anyone's going to end up on their backside you can bet it's going to be me.'

'Stop faffing around you two,' said Abi, grabbing her case and placing it on the end bed. 'We need to get this lot sorted so we can try and phone Toufiq about your bloody passport. Or had you forgotten about that?'

It didn't take them too long to unpack and put things away. Finishing first, Ann decided to make tea and coffee for them all and took hers out onto the balcony so she could have a quick smoke in peace.

As she stepped outside the steam from her mug of tea vapourised and her breath spiralled into the air, as an icy blast hit her. It was so cold she could almost smell it. A slightly earthy odour, reminiscent of smoke from a fire. As always in Istanbul, there was also the distinctly pervasive scent of traffic fumes.

Ann wrapped her hands around the warm mug, and leaning over the balcony took in more of their surroundings. It seemed to her curious, that at the same time as she could see the 15th-century outline of the Fatih Mosque, and architecture from the Byzantine and Ottoman periods everywhere, not 200 yards from the hotel, the Golden Arches of the local McDonalds infringed the eye line. Istanbul was indeed a city of contrast.

Beginning to feel the cold, Ann turned to go back inside but found the door wouldn't open. She rapped on the glass but then noticed that Abi and Ruth were sitting on the edges of their beds, drinking their coffee quite contentedly, their wide smiles showing they were clearly amused.

'Oh very funny! Open the bloody door and let me in.' The realisation that she had been deliberately locked out of the room began to dawn on her.

'What's it worth?' Ruth glanced over but carried on drinking her coffee.

'It's bloody freezing out here.'

'Well if you will go communing with nature when we've got important stuff to do.' giggled Abi.

'Enough now.'

Finally, they decided to open the door and let her back in.

'Ok, I guess I'd better bite the bullet and call Toufiq.' said Ruth. 'It's no good trying to ring on my mobile, the connection will be rubbish, so I'll have to use the hotel phone.'

Ruth dialled for an outside line and then tried to call Toufiq's number, without any success.

Abruptly, Ruth banged the phone back onto its holder. 'I can't get through. It's not even ringing.' She then exclaimed 'Oh shit! I've just realised, he said he might take the kids camping in the desert for a few days. There's no way he'll get a signal there.'

'Great.' said Abi. 'So what do we do now? We need to get hold of him somehow. Let me see if I can get hold of Mitri. He might be able to call or contact him.'

Unfortunately not. Neither husband was answering.

'Ann, you'll have to try Reza. See if he can get hold of either of them.' said Abi

'Third time lucky.' said Ann 'Though being the one who's got to explain everything is a pain in the rear, especially after you two volunteered me at passport control too.'

The sound of a long-distance ring tone could be heard by all three as they waited for an answer.

'Hello?'

'Hi, darling. We're here in Istanbul.'

'Oh good. How was the flight? All go OK? What's it like weather-wise?'

Ann took a deep breath. 'Yes, flight was good, but it's very cold here. Listen, we've got a bit of a problem. I need you to try and get hold of either Toufiq or Mitri as soon as you can.'

'Why? What problem?

'Welllll...' Ann crossed her fingers. 'Somehow, we're not sure how, but Ruth has managed to travel from Dubai on Jay's passport.'

'WHAT?'

This was not going so good!

'Are you winding me up?'

'No, honestly. We got stopped at immigration in Istanbul. I managed to get the visas stamped but then we realised that Ruth had the wrong passport with her. Don't ask me to explain everything now. We simply need you to try and get hold of either of them. We need Toufiq to courier Ruth's actual passport to the hotel as a matter of urgency. She's been given a seventy-two-hour visa but she has to report to airport security every morning until she produces her own passport.'

Complete silence.

'Hello. Are you still there?' Ann asked sheepishly.

'Yes, I'm still here but I'm not sure how I'm supposed to get hold of Toufiq. Wasn't he taking the kids camping for a couple of days? Are you sure you're not winding me up?'

Ann thrust the phone into Ruth's hand. 'You speak to him.'

Ruth wasn't sure about that. 'Hi, Reza,' she spoke quietly, 'I am so sorry about this, we have tried to contact Toufiq but can't get a connection. Mitri knows where he was going, so if you could maybe get hold of him at least?'

Immediately, Reza's tone was more conciliatory. 'Of course, leave it with me. Give me the phone number for the hotel and I'll see what I can do.'

'Thank you sooo much. We'll wait for a call. Do you want to talk to Ann again?'

'No that's OK. I'll speak to her later. Bye.'

'Phew! Oh my days, if that's how Reza reacts goodness knows what Toufiq is going to say.'

All they could do now was wait...

'There's not much more we can do for now. We can't go anywhere until we get that phone call and that could be a couple of hours so shall we go down and grab some lunch?' said Ann.

'Yes, that sounds like a plan,' answered Ruth. 'Don't forget I haven't had anything to eat, other than that bit of cake earlier. Unlike you two, scoffing all the chocolates etc whilst I was being 'detained.'

'Jealousy will get you nowhere,' Abi laughed. 'Come on then, let's go see what's available.'

The restaurant wasn't too busy and they were able to get a table quite easily. Almost immediately Miray came over to the table. 'How are you feeling now? Are you rested?'

'Better thanks,' said Ruth. 'We have to wait for a phone call before we can do anything else so we thought we'd grab some lunch.'

'Certainly. I will bring you some menus.'

It was difficult to decide on what to eat as the list was endless and it all looked fabulous.

'I don't know what I want,' said Ruth.

'Apart from your passport.' Ann responded with a smirk.

'Don't start,' answered Ruth. 'Can we get something to eat now, before I keel over?'

'Drama queen.' said Abi. 'Listen, I don't know what I want either so how about we go for a meze, for now, that way we'll get a good mix to keep us going till this evening.'

'Oooh yes! I like that idea.' said Ann.

'Right then, let's do that.' said Ruth. 'Miray… Miray,' she called 'Can we order now please?'

Miray was at the table in a flash. 'Yes ladies, what is your pleasure?'

'Can we get a Meze please?' asked Ruth.

'Of course. Whatever you wish. Do you have any preference? Or shall I bring a selection of hot and cold for all of you?'

'Yes, that would be a good idea.' said Ruth. 'Otherwise, we could be here all day trying to decide.'

'Can't wait for this,' said Ann 'Love a good meze.'

When the food began to arrive the three were glad the table was a big one – there was so much food. Şakşuka, otherwise known as Baba Ganoush (eggplant), Hayduri (Yoghurt & Dill), Hummus, Çöp Şiş (lamb kebab), Dolma (vine leaves), Kız güzeli (Beetroot dip), Mixed Olive salad all served with Bazlama (Turkish Flatbreads).

'Oh lord, if this is what we're going to be eating for the rest of the week we'll be as big as houses by the time we get back.' said Ruth.

'If you get back!' Abi laughed.

They began to tuck in, relishing every mouthful, and for once there was relative silence – for a very short time.

'Hey look at her.' said Abi

'Who?' asked Ann.

'Her, over there. Do you reckon she's a secret agent?'

'What?' Ruth spluttered, almost spilling her food.

'Look at her, she's clearly acting suspiciously.'

'How do you work that one out?' asked Ann.

'She's definitely got that *look* about her.'

'What look?' asked Ann again.

'You know, tha*t 'I'm a secret agent look'*.'

'You're off your trolley,' said Ann. 'She has nothing of the sort.'

'Anyway, I think she does.' Abi scrunched up her eyes and drew her neck into her shoulders.

Ruth gave Abi one of *her* looks. 'I think you're suffering from sleep deprivation. The poor girl's merely sitting there, drinking her coffee and minding her own business.'

'Yes, but it's the way she's merely sitting there.'

'So how would you like her to sit?' Ann enquired.

'Not like that!'

Abi, now bored with the *secret agent* scenario, turned her attentions elsewhere to a youngish couple across the room. 'What about those two? Bet they're having an affair.'

Again, Ruth spluttered. 'Oh for crying out loud. How did you reach that conclusion?'

'Because they're talking to each other and holding hands, they can't be married.'

'So, because you and Mitri don't speak to each other or hold hands when you're out, you think it applies to all married couples? Anyway, she's wearing a wedding ring,' replied Ruth.

'Yes she is but I bet he didn't give it to her.'

Ann laughed. 'Oh, I see, we're having another one of those 'let's make up stories' moments are we?'

Abi only grinned in reply.

Miray re-appeared. 'How was everything ladies? Can I get you anything else?'

'Wonderful, thank you,' Ruth answered. 'No, I think we've all had enough for now.'

'Very good. Can I get your table cleared for you?'

'Yes, thank you,' said Ruth.

'Right, you two, I don't know about you but I could do with a little power nap so I'm going back upstairs. You coming?' said Ann.

'Guess we can't do a lot till we get that phone call, it's been a couple of hours now, surely it won't take Mitri or Reza much longer to get hold of Toufiq? Besides which I don't think I can take any more of your idiocy,' Ruth said, pointedly looking at Abi.

Back in their room Ann promptly collapsed onto the bed and was asleep within minutes, much to the discernment of Abi. 'How does she do it? Exactly how?'

'Obviously, she has a clear conscience,' answered Ruth, who was still feeling a little guilty about her lack of organisation. 'I'm going to try and get some shut-eye as well.' She too was asleep very quickly.

Wonderful thought Abi *that leaves me then*, taking out her book to read as she lay down on her bed. She'd managed about twenty pages when she felt her eyes closing and she finally drifted off…

Ann was in the midst of a dream, and somewhere, in the distance, she could hear bells ringing incessantly. *What the… maybe it's a fire or burglar alarm going off. I suppose I better take a look…* but she soon realised that it was neither, as she slowly came round from her slumbers to hear the phone ringing.

Groggily, she sat up and reached for the phone. 'Hello,' she said hesitantly, not sure whether she was awake or still dreaming.

'Hello madam. This is Miray – we have a call for you.'

'Oh, thank you, please put them through,' said Ann, reaching across and giving Ruth a hefty shove. 'Oi. Ruth. Wake up. There's a phone call, it could be Toufiq.'

'What the…stop shoving me.' Ruth never was good when she first woke up. She could hear Ann mumbling in the background.

'Hello?' said Ann.

She quickly handed the phone to Ruth on hearing Toufiq's voice at the other end of the line. He sounded less than impressed, and as Ruth took the phone from her she knew there was going to be trouble.

'Hello…?' said Ruth. 'Oh-oh, hi Toufiq. You and the kids having a good time?' (Ann winced at this - *surely not the best thing to say under the circumstances* - as demonstrated by the torrent of Arabic profanities she could hear coming down the line) 'Yes, yes' continued Ruth 'I know. I know. OK, you've made your point but I can't do much to change it can I? I don't know how it happened. If I knew how it happened then it wouldn't have happened would it, cos I'd have realised before it happened and not brought the wrong passport but the right one.' (*Sort of makes sense,* thought Ann, continuing to listen in.)

Abi by this point was 'back in the room' and listening intently.

'Ok, so when do you think you can get my passport to the courier?'

'What? No, no, no!' (Ann and Abi were getting a bit concerned at the look on Ruth's face.)

Toufiq's voice… indistinct.

'Surely there must be a way?'

Toufiq… still indistinct.

'Well, that's rubbish then.'

Toufiq… (one way conversations are hard to understand.)

'Don't you know anybody? So, not much I can do then is there? Okay, okay, please let me know as soon as you can. Yes, okay, bye for now.' Ruth put the phone down and promptly burst into tears.

'What's up? asked Ann.

'We forgot it's the Eid holiday and everywhere is closed, so he can't even get to a courier for two days,' said Ruth.

'Clearly, you might have forgotten but we hadn't,' said Abi sarcastically, smirking for good measure.

'That's nasty,' cried Ruth. 'What am I going to do?'

'Nothing basically' said Ann 'We'll have to wait, make sure we report to the airport every morning, as early as possible, and make the most of the days as much as we can.'

'Guess so.' Ruth replied.

Chapter 6

The Nightclub

Ann was on the balcony again, having a cigarette and a think. *Okay. Maybe this isn't quite the start we were expecting. Still, it's not all doom and gloom. At least we can do a bit of sightseeing once we've been to the airport.* Looking at her watch she saw it was a little after six o'clock. *We need to get out of the hotel tonight and have a good time, just forget about today with all its problems.* She turned and went back into the room.

'Right you two. We're going out.' She announced.

'Out where?' asked Abi.

'I don't know. Let's all get showered and changed. The first one ready can go downstairs and see if reception has any suggestions.'

'As it's your idea,' said Abi 'you get ready first.'

Abi didn't need to repeat it. Ann couldn't wait to get out of her clothes and into something fresh, she'd been wearing the same thing for almost twenty-four hours. The bathroom was huge and invitingly temperate. *Oh bliss!* she thought as the warm water hit her body, easing all the aches and pains she was feeling from the stresses of the day. It never took her long to shower so she was soon out and drying herself off.

'Bloody hell that was quick,' said Abi, as Ann reappeared in the room.

'Unlike you, I don't mess about. In and out, that's me.'

'I could say something to that.' said Abi giving Ann a suggestive smirk.

'So what are we wearing tonight? Out, out stuff or only out stuff?' asked Ann.

'As we don't know where we're going I would suggest out plus,' said Ruth.

'What the hell is out plus?' Abi and Ann asked almost in unison.

'Comfortable but smart, without being too dressy,' said Ruth.

'New one on me,' said Abi 'But if you say so it must be true.'

'Layers I think,' said Ann. 'It's cold out so need to be warm, but it might be warm where we end up so need to be cool.'

'Oh, my days. Seriously? Do you always overthink things?' said Abi.

'I merely like to be prepared for all eventualities, unlike someone else I could mention,' she said glancing at Ruth who pretended to be reading her book and completely ignored the comment.

Half an hour later Ann was downstairs at the reception desk. Miray had left for the night and there was a young man on duty. Ann approached him and said, 'Good evening.'

'Good evening madam. How may I help you?'

'My friends and I arrived this morning and we've had a bit of a stressful day. We want to go out this evening, relax and have a good time. Somewhere maybe with music and where we can also eat. We wondered whether you might have any suggestions?'

'Aaah. You're the English ladies with no passport, yes?'

Bloody hell, is that how we're going to be known now?
Ann thought to herself but smiled sweetly as she
answered 'Yes. That's us.'

'Very sorry to hear of your problems madam.
Miray told me about it before she left. Probably the
best place you could go for good food and music, that
isn't too far, is the Kervansaray, it's about twenty
minutes from here by taxi. The food is excellent and
they have live singers and music. Very nice.'

'Perfect. That sounds wonderful. Would you
be able to get us a taxi to take us there?'

'Of course madam. Let me know when you
are ready.'

'Great, thank you. Do we need to book or
can we simply turn up?'

'It is very popular so it is good to book first.'

'Can you do that for us?'

'Of course, madam, for what time would you
like the table?' he asked as he lifted the phone.

Looking at her watch Ann saw it was already
approaching seven o'clock. 'What time do they stop
serving food?' she asked.

'Not until midnight madam.'

'In that case for around eight-thirty if that's possible.'

'Certainly madam,' he said as he dialled the number and spoke in Turkish. 'All booked for eight-thirty madam.'

'Thank you. I think I'll wait over there for my friends,' she pointed to the bar area.

Seating herself at a table Ann called the waiter over and ordered herself a spiced rum with coke. She daren't even think about having a Raki, she'd be *squiffy* before they even left the hotel. They weren't big drinkers normally, but this wasn't normal, and anyway, they were on holiday. Settling back into her seat, feeling quite relaxed now she'd showered and changed, she drank in her surroundings.

Despite the time of year, and the cold weather, lots of people were around, all nationalities it seemed from the snippets of conversation she could hear, but then again Istanbul was a very cosmopolitan city and she could imagine it would probably be busy all year round, not only with tourists but with business people too. There was so much to see and do here it wouldn't matter that it was cold.

'Don't wait for us will you?' she heard, as the dulcet tones of Ruth's voice reached her ears.

'What did you expect me to do, sit here like a lemon waiting for you?'

'How many have you had?' asked Abi.

'It's my first. Why? What's it to you?'

'So we know if we're going to have to carry you home.' Abi said.

'You'll be the one we'll be carrying home if you get started on the Black Russians.'

'Will someone please get me a bloody drink,' pleaded Ruth.

Drinks ordered, they sat around the table discussing the proposed evening.

'So did they have any suggestions?' asked Ruth.

'Yes. Some place called Kervansaray. It's a nightclub stroke music venue that apparently serves excellent food and is only about twenty minutes away. I've booked us a table for eight-thirty and a taxi is picking us up in about thirty minutes. So you'd better get those drinks down you.'

'I feel so much better now that I've had a sleep and shower. Let's forget about everything else and have a good time tonight. Tomorrow we can stay close to the hotel so we don't have to go to the airport too early,' said Ruth.

'Good idea,' said Abi 'There's plenty to do nearby.'

'We could have a mooch around Taksim Square, take a look round the shops, and then meander down to the water's edge and along the Bosphorus, if there's time. Then we can find somewhere around Taksim to eat in the evening,' suggested Ann.

'Sounds like a plan,' agreed Abi.

The reception guy, Deniz, appeared at their table to tell them their taxi was waiting outside.

'I have told him where to take you,' he said.

'Thank you,' said Ruth.

Ann and Abi had walked on ahead and were getting into the back seat of the taxi when Ruth caught up with them.

'How come I'm in the front?' asked Ruth.

'Snooze you lose,' said Abi, smiling wickedly.

Ruth, reluctantly, climbed into the front seat.

'Do you speak English?' Abi asked the taxi driver who slowly shook his head. 'Arabic?' He nodded. 'Aywa.' (Yes)

'There you go then Ruth. That's why you're in the front – you speak the best Arabic,' said Ann.

Ruth wasn't convinced but didn't have much choice, so she struck up a conversation with the driver, whose name turned out to be Yusuf. Ann and Abi couldn't join in because Ann spoke no Arabic other than rudimentary words and phrases and Abi, slightly better, was still nowhere near as fluent as Ruth.

The journey did only take around twenty minutes and they were soon at the venue. As they all got out of the cab Ruth turned back to speak to Yusuf again, which surprised Ann and Abi as he hadn't called her back.

'So what was that all about?' asked Ann 'You setting yourself up then?'

'Don't be bloody ridiculous,' Ruth retorted 'I was asking him if he could pick us up, later on, to take us back. We might not be so lucky next time to find a driver who can speak either English or Arabic. Unless you've got any other suggestions.'

'Oh right,' said Ann feeling suitably chastened 'And?'

'He'll be back here at around twelve-ish to pick us up. That should be Ok shouldn't it?'

'I would have thought so,' said Abi.

With this, they headed off to the entrance of the club. From the outside, it didn't look too impressive, located in an area with poor street lighting, crumbling paintwork, and appeared quite small, but once inside it was a different story. It was massive, a little like the Tardis! There was a semi-circular centre stage with long tables radiating outwards from it. The place was heaving and waiters were scurrying around with enormous trays of food and drinks. On stage, a D.J. was providing the tunes and the three looked at each other with some disappointment.

'I thought there was live music?' said Abi.

'That's what Deniz said. Maybe he's just filling in between acts. If this place is open till two o'clock maybe they mix it up a bit,' Ann said, fingers crossed behind her back.

Unsure where to go (they couldn't see any free tables) they stood, looking around for a clue. A waiter seemed to materialise out of nowhere. 'Can I help you, ladies? Do you have a booking?' All three were relieved to learn he spoke English.

'Yes,' said Ann 'Deniz from the Hotel Ayrias called about an hour ago to book it for us.'

'Ah yes. Let me go and check for you.'

'At least I hope he did,' Ann was a little concerned but the waiter soon came back and told them to follow him. Ann breathed a sigh of relief.

The waiter took them to a table almost in the centre of the stage area where there were three spaces visible along one side. What appeared to be a mix of nationalities (from the conversations taking place) took up the rest of the table and adjoining tables were occupied by a very large group of Japanese tourists and a few locals.

'That's always a good sign,' said Ann 'If locals use a place it's usually pretty good.'

Almost immediately after being seated the waiter was back with trays of meze of all descriptions. Understandable, given the size of the audience, that it was a pre-set menu. Once he had placed the food in front of them he asked for their drinks order. Cocktails were on offer but they weren't particularly cocktail drinkers, so Ann stayed with her spiced rum,

Abi with her Black Russian and Ruth decided on Bacardi and coke.

The food, as they had been told, was delicious and plentiful. It suited them all because there were lots of choices, and Abi could be quite a fussy eater.

At around nine-fifteen the D.J. stopped, the lights went down and the audience became hushed as the M.C. appeared and introduced the live artist. It wasn't a name any of them were familiar with but he appeared to be known to many of the crowd as they cheered loudly.

'This looks OK then, doesn't it?' said Abi. 'Obviously, someone well known locally. Let's hope he's good.'

The backing musicians started up as the singer, let's call him Micael, launched into a rendition of Tony Bennett's The Lady is a Tramp – and he was good!

Over the next fifteen minutes or so he belted out several similar tunes and the crowd was loving it, clapping and cheering with gusto. Then he started calling people out from the audience to join him on stage. They tried but unfortunately, many of them were not good singers.

It went the same way each time. The audience member would get up on stage and discuss a song to sing. Micael would walk ahead singing the first few bars and they would join in from behind. For the most part, Micael would, at some point, pull a face at the audience as if to say *Clearly they shouldn't give up their day job!*. It was all done in good humour and accepted as such. The audience loved it.

There came a point in the evening, after singing solo for a while, that Micael was again asking for volunteers. Ann and Abi both had the same thought at the same time as they simultaneously leant back in their chairs, winked at each other, nodded, and then hands raised, pointed fingers at Ruth, who was sitting between them, blissfully unaware of what was happening.

Micael noticed them and came to the front of the stage, extending his hand towards Ruth, who shrank back in horror.

'No. No. No,' she said.

'Yes. Yes. Yes,' said Abi and Ann in unison. 'Go on. It's only a bit of fun.'

After much goading and bribery, Ruth finally stood up and walked towards the stage in her inimitable slinky fashion, all the while glaring back at

Ann and Abi who were laughing hysterically. The audience clapped and cheered her onto the stage where the usual discussion took place as to the choice of song.

'Ha! this should be good,' said Ann.

'Yep,' agreed Abi.

They knew what was coming.

Micael did his usual thing, handing a mike to Ruth and then walking ahead of her to the tune of John Denver's Leaving on a jet plane. Quite ironic when you think about it.

Micael was walking towards the audience, with the intro playing in the background, as he launched into the first verse. 'All my bags.....' As he reached the second verse Ruth began to sing 'So kiss me....' which halted Micael in his stride, a look of total shock on his face, he turned as Ruth continued to sing. The audience was on their feet, cheering and clapping, and Micael dropped his mike, stood to one side, and gestured for Ruth to take centre stage.

What Abi and Ann knew was that Ruth was a professionally trained singer and had made her living at it before she married Toufiq and had her family. She had the most beautiful, soulful voice you could imagine.

Micael remained silent until the very last verse.

Ruth finally managed to get off the stage after countless encores and shouts for more, and rejoined Ann and Abi at their table, where everyone stood up and applauded her as she took her seat.

'I am going to bloody kill you two!'

Ann and Abi both laughed.

Around ten minutes later their waiter reappeared carrying the biggest tray of fresh fruit any of them had seen, followed by another waiter with a bottle of champagne and three glasses in his hand.

Finally, the manager of the venue appeared. 'Madam,' he said addressing Ruth 'the champagne is from Micael, the fruit is from the management, and your bill tonight has been paid by your Japanese friends. Everything else tonight is also on the house. We have never had such a response before to an audience member. Thank you for singing for us.'

Ruth, Ann, and Abi looked at each other in disbelief.

'Wow. That is so unbelievably generous. Thank you so much.'

'Madam,' said the manager 'the pleasure, I assure you, is entirely ours.'

'You still gonna kill us?' asked Ann, looking at Ruth with a cheesy grin.

'Nah! She'll manage to get us back some other way,' Abi countered.

The rest of the evening was almost as unbelievable. Of course, they shared the proceeds of their gift with the rest of their table and before they knew it it was almost midnight and time to leave. (Where was Cinderella when you needed her?)

As they stood up to go, there was yet another round of spontaneous applause that followed them, all the way out.

'Fabulous. That was some night. Let's hope Yusuf is waiting for us. I'm absolutely knackered,' said Ann.

'Me too,' said Abi.

'Don't even go there,' said Ruth but with a smile.

Yusuf, as promised, was waiting outside for them and within twenty-five minutes they were back at the hotel. They went straight to their room and in

63

less than fifteen minutes all three were tucked up in bed, exhausted from the day they'd had.

Chapter 7

Taksim

The next morning Ann was up first. Despite the traumas of the day before, in addition to the late-night, she felt surprisingly refreshed. Abi and Ruth were still in the land of nod.

She filled the kettle with the bottled water they had bought the evening before, and then sat, watching it, waiting for it to boil. Fatal! It didn't. Nothing was happening. *Oh for crying out loud, now what?* She thought to herself, not taking in that the reason the kettle wasn't doing its thing was that she hadn't actually turned it on. Finally, she realised. *Thank god those two are still snoring. I would have got stick for that basic mistake. Err! Hang on a minute – what am I worrying about, at least I remembered my passport.*

Having given the kettle permission to bubble by switching it on, she waited for it to boil and made her tea. Ann wasn't anywhere near human until she'd had at least two cups of tea in the morning.

She wandered over to the balcony door, trying very hard to open it without waking anyone, but had nowhere to put her cup (*It's the little things*) which she then placed on the floor. Slowly she turned the key and pushed the door. *Bloody hell. I thought this was Istanbul, not Siberia!* She had to try and open/close it as quickly as possible so as not to disturb the others but she would need her coat if she didn't want to get hypothermia.

Creeping back across the room she found her coat, grabbed her tea, pushed the door hard, and promptly dropped her cup.

Abi sat up with a start. 'What the hell? What are you doing? Why have you got your coat on? Why is it bloody freezing in here?' she stopped to draw breath and sat up in bed. Fully awake almost immediately.

'I was going to go outside to drink my tea so I didn't wake you but I dropped my cup.'

'Huh! That plan didn't go too good then did it?' said Abi.

A sleepy voice could be heard coming from underneath the blankets 'Why is everyone making soooo much noise?'

'Silly mare is at it already and it's not even (*glancing at her watch*) SEVEN O'CLOCK. It's not even seven o'clock? It's still the middle of the night,' Abi was prone to exaggerate.

'I woke up early and so thought I should get up so we can get an early breakfast before we go to the airport,' Ann was frantically trying to wipe up the spilt tea.

At this, Ruth, who had been lying very still and saying nothing, suddenly leapt from the bed. 'Oh crap, I forgot about that. Yes, we'd better get moving or the day will be gone.'

'Gone? Gone where?' said Abi 'I need coffee before I can even think about getting up.'

'Maybe this will help move you,' Ann threw the balcony door open wide and the bitterly cold January air hit the room.

'Aaaargh. Shut that door!'

'Who do you think you are?' asked Ruth. 'Larry Grayson?'

'Very funny. Are we going to have another one of *those* days today?'

'Don't know what you mean,' said Ruth innocently, knowing exactly what Abi was getting at.

Eventually, Abi managed to prise herself out of bed.

Forty minutes later the three friends, now dressed for the cold, but carrying their coats, arrived in the hotel restaurant where a help-yourself buffet was laid out with hot and cold dishes of all descriptions. There were black and green olives, cucumbers, cured meats, dips and sauces, eggs, fresh cheeses and tomatoes, fresh-baked bread, fruit preserves and jams, honey, pastries, and sweet butter. It looked fabulous, tasted even better, and was plentiful enough to set them up for the day ahead.

While Abi and Ann grabbed second cups of tea and coffee (Ann still doesn't like coffee) Ruth went across to reception where Miray, the female receptionist who had greeted them the day before, was back on duty.

'Yes madam. How can I help?'

'Could you possibly get us a taxi to take us to the airport?'

'Oh madam, you are leaving us so soon?'

'No, no. I have to report to the security office every day until my passport arrives.'

'Ahh, I see. That is trouble for you no? Yes, I will do that for you no problem.'

Ruth wasn't sure what she meant by trouble but assumed she meant inconvenience.

Going back to the restaurant Ruth was silently praying that there would be no more '*trouble*' today.

Again, the journey took longer than they'd hoped because it was still rush hour, and though Turkish drivers are not among the worst in the world, they seemed to neglect basic traffic rules, squeezing themselves into the smallest space available, swerving across the roads, and blocking emergency lanes.

'I don't know how they don't have more accidents,' Ruth was feeling a little nervous. 'They're all mad.'

Ann grabbed hold of the door handle as the driver took a sudden left turn, narrowly missing a car that was stopped in the middle of the road meaning he then had to swerve to avoid it.

They eventually arrived safely but not without several near misses, and while Ruth, reluctantly, went off on her own to find the security office to check-in,

Ann and Abi sat outside waiting, watching all the comings and goings. The constant traffic could be heard all around them and with it came the choking pollution of diesel and petrol, a distinct odour of sulphur in the air.

'Hope she's not going to be too long,' said Abi as the cold of the morning began to penetrate, despite her being wrapped up like an arctic explorer.

'Everything crossed they haven't changed their minds.'

'Oh don't. How long should we wait before we go search for her?' Abi asked.

'I don't think there will be a problem. The trouble with Ruth is she looks guilty even when she hasn't done anything.'

Luckily, Ruth only had to go to the arrivals section of the airport on the ground floor so the likelihood of her getting lost, *in theory*, was minimal. Unfortunately, her sense of direction was less than perfect and she did. (Get lost that is).

It must be around here somewhere. Ruth muttered to herself. *I remember seeing that sign yesterday* ('that' sign was one of many scattered throughout the arrivals hall). *Bugger, why does it all look the same?* (Because it is?)

It's no good, I'm going to have to try and find someone to help. Looking for the sign for security, or someone who looked like they could converse in English, Ruth wandered, somewhat aimlessly, stopping and speaking to several people until she found someone who pointed to a door, located inside the arrivals hall entrance, which stated 'güvenlik' (Security). *How did I miss that?*

It didn't take very long. Once she had 'signed in' and shown her seventy-two-hour visa she was free to go. Luckily, the same security guards from the day before were on duty and recognised her.

All she had to now was remember where she had left Ann and Abi waiting, but instead of turning right out of the security office towards the exit, she turned left and again found herself seeing 'that' sign everywhere 'danışma' (which roughly translated means information desk.).

'Where are you going you silly mare?' Ann's voice reached Ruth's ears.

'Coming to find you and Abi.'

'Clearly, you won't find us over there,' Ann was getting a teeny bit frustrated.

'We thought we'd come in to look for you and noticed you coming out of the security office. Why didn't you head for the exit?' asked Abi.

'I thought I was,' said Ruth 'but I couldn't see any signs.'

Ann spun her round to face the opposite direction. 'See that big sign there that says çıkış?'

'Err, yes but I don't know what that means,' pleaded Ruth.

'Try looking *just* underneath that BIG word, you'll see another word. What does that say?'

Sheepishly Ruth said 'Exit.'

'Exactly!'

Abi simply rolled her eyes.

Taking an arm each, they steered Ruth towards the exit, in case she disappeared again, and then, once outside, they headed towards the taxi rank.

Finding a cab quite easily they asked the driver to take them to Beyoğlu, the district for Taksim Square. They knew this was where the main shopping and entertainment area of Istanbul was located and they were quite excited at the prospect of whiling away a few hours window shopping, sightseeing, and having something to eat in one of the many restaurants later on in the evening.

'Let's hope the traffic has quieted down a bit,' said Ann. 'Not sure if my nerves can stand another journey like this morning.'

Survival of the fittest looks to be the best way to describe rush hour traffic in Istanbul. As soon as traffic jams start building up, drivers duck and dive trying to find alternative roads, and once found, they race through them trying to catch up on time already lost. Lane markings are taken as being for decorative purposes only and it doesn't take long for a three-lane road to transform itself into a five-lane one. The noise is raucous too; the rule seeming to be to use the car's horn as much as possible. It doesn't make the journey any smoother but appears to work wonders at releasing drivers' stress.

Traffic was a little lighter but the journey was no less stressful. Eventually, they arrived at Taksim Square. To say it was busy was indeed an understatement. People thronged together everywhere and it would be easy to get carried along with the crowd, even if the direction wasn't the one you wanted to go in.

'Wow! Look at this lot,' said Abi looking around. 'So many shops.'

'Yes, and so many people. Rule number one,' said Ann looking directly at Ruth 'Stay together. No wandering off. We'll never find each other again in these crowds. OK?'

'OK bossyboots,' Ruth answered. Feeling a lot happier now that her trip to report to security had gone (almost) without a hitch.

Ann was becoming worried because Ruth had her mischievous look on her face now that she knew she was safe (for the time being at least) from arrest or deportation. *Oh god, I hope she behaves herself!*

'So, what shall we do?' said Abi. 'Meander down the main street, have a look at the shops and stuff, have a little stroll down some of the side streets for a while, go right to the end, maybe have that stroll along by the Bosphorous and then get the tram back later on this evening?'

'Suits me,' said Ann 'It'll take a good few hours to walk the whole length, especially if we're going to be popping in and out of shops, *together,* Ruth.'

'That's fine,' said Ruth who was strolling along without a care in the world.

Ann and Abi were engrossed in looking at the shop windows and little street cafés along the way, admiring all the colourful shop displays and the stunning architecture they passed. They, only briefly, took their eyes off of Ruth but she was still within view. It wasn't so much that she wasn't right next to them that worried Ann, but what she could hear Ruth saying, albeit quietly.

'What the…? Is she *trying* to get us arrested?' Ann turned to Abi 'Can you hear what she's saying?'

Ruth's words drifted back to them, quietly but clearly. *Got any dope? Got any dope to sell? Got any dope?*

'RUTH!!!' cried Ann.

'What?'

'What are you doing?'

'Only checking,' Ruth grinned.

Ann knew then that she was being wound up deliberately. 'Honestly, it's not funny. Any one of those people could be plain-clothed police. You could get yourself into all sorts of trouble as if you're not in enough already.'

'Don't be such a party pooper,' said Ruth

'She's right though Ruth,' Abi agreed.

'OK. OK. I'll stop. But you never know do you?' Again, that mischievous smile.

With Ann and Abi keeping a very close eye on Ruth, for the next couple of hours, the three friends wandered in and out of shops, stopping for a drink in one or two of the many cafes along the way. The aromas in the air were tantalising, assaulting the senses at every corner. Fresh coffee, baklava, kebabs being turned outside street cafes, the odour of fresh-baked flatbreads, and very occasionally, the scent of Lemon Cologne emanating from one of the old-fashioned barbershops down some of the smaller side streets. They checked out the Flower Passage (Cicek Pasaji) where refugees used to sell flowers but which was now an arcade with restaurants, famous for mezes, raki, and gypsy dancing. They strolled along the bustling Nevizade Street renowned for its night-time entertainment and French Street, replicating the café culture of Paris, providing all things French in food and wine at its pavement cafés, with colourful umbrellas standing at each table. They continued, leisurely crisscrossing Istiklal Avenue until they reached the very southern end of the famous street. By which time it had grown dark.

'God I'm exhausted,' said Ann 'I've never seen so many people in one place, and it's January. What must it be like in summer?'

'Fabulous, isn't it,' said Abi.

'Still no dope though,' grinned Ruth.

'Shall we head back up now then? We can get the tram, jump off halfway and go find a restaurant down one of the side streets. I don't know about you two but all that walking has made me hungry,' said Ann.

'I'm getting that way,' Ruth answered.

'Ok but I don't want a great big meal,' Abi not only didn't sleep; she also didn't eat very much either.

They hopped on the tram at Tünel Square and enjoyed the journey back up Istiklal Avenue. It was slow going, as the conductor had to keep ringing the bell to clear pedestrians out of the way, but halfway up they were able to jump off at Galatasaray Square to give them more choice of eateries and headed away from the main drag down the side streets.

'There's so much choice,' said Abi. 'Not sure it will matter which one we go to though.'

'Yes, you're probably right,' said Ruth. 'Come on, let's go in here, it looks OK.'

'Let's see if we can find a window table upstairs,' said Ann. 'We'll be able to watch the comings and goings then, get a better view.'

Making their way up to the first floor it became apparent that eating early wasn't the done thing in Istanbul, as the restaurant was almost empty. There were plenty of tables available, so they headed for one overlooking the street.

A waiter appeared straight away and gave them each a menu. Luckily for them, despite being written in Turkish (which none of them could read) they also had photos of the meals.

'This is going to be exciting,' said Abi, smiling. 'Let's hope they are what they look like or we could have a problem.'

'I quite fancy an apple tea,' said Ann. 'They're great.'

'Not tried one of those before,' said Ruth. 'I'll have one too.'

'OK, so will I,' Abi joined in.

'WHAT? No coffee?' asked Ann. 'Are you ill?'

'Shut up. I do drink other things.'

Catching the attention of the waiter, Ruth called him over and asked for three apple teas. There was a completely blank look on his face. So, she tried again. Same response. He spoke to her, in Turkish, and it was Ruth's turn to look blank.

'What's he saying?' she asked, looking at Ann and Abi hopefully.

'How the bloody hell do I know?' Ann replied. 'I don't speak Turkish, that's what I have Reza for.'

'Ask him if he speaks English,' Abi suggested.

'Unbelievable! If he spoke English he would have known what Ruth was asking him in the first place. Doh!'

'No need to be nasty,' Abi replied.

'What are we going to do then?' Ruth asked.

They looked around and noticed a man sitting a couple of tables away, who was talking on his phone. 'Let's see if he speaks English,' suggested Ann.

'Excuse me... Excuse me,' called Ann, trying to get his attention. He must have heard her because he looked over at their table. 'Do you speak English?'

'A little,' he said.

'Oh good. We are trying to order three apple teas but the waiter doesn't seem to speak English and we don't speak Turkish. Can you help us?'

'Ah. Yes, no problem,' he said, calling the waiter over to his table. 'Three apple teas for the ladies,' he asked, with a strong Turkish accent but in English.

They all looked at each other in disbelief as the waiter disappeared and very quickly reappeared carrying three apple teas.

All three struggled to suppress their giggles as he placed them on the table.

'Unbelievable,' said Abi, and again they all had to try very hard not to laugh.

Ordering food, in comparison, was relatively easy as they only had to point to the pictures on the menu. 'Fingers crossed it is, actually, chicken,' said Ann. They had all decided, for simplicity's sake, to order the same, chicken kebab with salad.

For the next 10 minutes or so they engaged in one of their favourite pastimes – people watching. Making up lives and stories for the people strolling up and down in the street below and those they could see through the windows of the restaurants and cafes on the opposite side of the street.

'What do you reckon about him then? asked Abi.

'Who?' questioned Ann, looking around her.

'Him, the one who ordered our tea.'

Ann glanced in his direction. 'He looks a bit suss to me; his eyes are too close together for my liking. I reckon he's a spy or a private detective.'

Ruth nearly choked on her tea. 'How the hell do you work that one out? He looks perfectly ordinary to me.'

'Keep watching, you'll see what I mean in a minute. He's constantly on his phone but speaking very quietly, and he keeps looking out of the window.'

'What? Like us you mean?'

Abi nudged Ruth as '*the man*' slowly got up from his seat and moved closer to the window. 'Yes, yes I can see her,' he whispered into his phone. 'No, no, she seems to be alone at the moment.'

'THERE! I told you so,' Ann felt vindicated.

At this point Abi craned her neck, looking out of the window to try and find out who it was '*the man*' was keeping an eye on, but there were so many people around, it was impossible to tell. 'Can either of you make out who it is?' she whispered.

'What about her? The one over there in the red top with blond hair?' ventured Ann.

'Too obvious. Anyway, she's not on her own,' Ruth answered. 'She was with some bloke a minute ago, maybe he's gone to pay the bill or something?'

'I think it's the one behind her, she's got blond hair too but I haven't seen her with anyone so far,' suggested Abi.

The man then moved away from the window back to his original seat. 'I need to be careful she doesn't catch sight of me. I'll keep watching and check in again in about half an hour.'

They all looked at each other, stifling laughs as they watched *the man* watching whoever he was watching.

The waiter reappeared with their food, which looked and smelt amazing, and placed it in front of them. Before he could disappear again Abi asked if anyone wanted more tea, both Ruth and Ann said yes, but instead of trying to communicate their order in either English or Turkish, Abi simply held up her little tulip-shaped glass, pointed to it, and held up three fingers. The waiter nodded and left.

'That's one way of doing it,' Ruth grinned. 'Let's hope he understood. Just as well we didn't only want two.'

They tucked into the chicken and salad, all ravenous as they hadn't eaten since breakfast.

'Mmmm, delicious. Yours OK?' asked Ruth.

'Very nice,' Ann replied.

'Nice, but too much for me, I won't eat all of this,' Abi answered.

They ate in silence, continuing to glance across the street now and then looking for likely suspects who might be being watched by '*the man.*'

'There…there...' Abi suddenly exclaimed, trying to keep her voice low. 'The older woman with the brown hair and thick jumper. She's definitely on her own and she looks suspicious too. She keeps looking around her.'

'Maybe…' as Ann was about to express her opinion '*the man*' moved closer to the window again, holding his phone close to his mouth.

'Yes, she's still there, alone. No wait, she's putting her coat on. I think she's about to leave. Yes, yes I'm on my way. I'll call later if there's anything to report.' With that he grabbed his coat and abruptly left the restaurant, appearing in seconds on the street below as the '*older woman*' suddenly left the restaurant opposite and started heading towards Taksim Square.

'Oh blimey. Do you think we need to report this to anyone?' Ruth suggested.

'Report what? To whom?' Abi enquired, giving her a quizzical look. 'We don't know what it's all about, maybe he is a private detective and so far he hasn't done anything wrong. Unless we all leave now and follow them both, we won't find out and I don't know about you two but my little legs don't work that fast.'

'I'm with Abi on this,' Ann piped up. 'We can't go interfering, especially here, you don't know what you might be getting us involved in. Anyway, if we did report it and someone came, what could we actually tell them. Could you honestly describe either of them accurately? *"Oh yes officer his eyes were too close together and she was maybe in her 40's or 50's with brown hair? They went that way!"* Seriously, forget it.'

'Ok, if you're sure?'

All the excitement over they finished their food in relative silence.

'OK, what now?' asked Abi, once the waiter had cleared the plates away. 'It's still quite early. What do you want to do now?'

'Let's leave and maybe go find a café somewhere, let the food go down a bit, and have a hot drink?' suggested Ann.

'Yeah OK. Sounds good,' said Abi.

Outside in the street, the temperature had dropped further and with seemingly fewer people around, the chill of the night could readily be felt.

They walked through the darkened streets, looking closely at some of the cafes to find one that seemed suitable.

'This one looks OK. Clean and not too busy. I just want to get inside out of the cold,' Ann always seemed to be the one to feel the cold the most.

Inside the café was warm and welcoming, several young waiters hovering around waiting for custom. One of them was at the table as soon as they sat down.

'English?' he asked tentatively.

Oh great, at least we won't have to find an interpreter in here, thought Ruth. 'Yes,' she replied. *He better not mention passports!!!*

Abi and Ruth ordered coffee and Ann plumped for a mint tea this time. The drinks arrived almost as quickly as the waiter had.

'You are here on holiday?' asked the waiter.

'Just for a few days,' said Ruth

'From which part of England do you come?'

'From London originally, but now we all live in Dubai,' Ruth said.

'Dubai? This is…şaşılacak. How do you say? Wonderful,' he enthused. 'Always I wanted to go there. It is very hot and beautiful, yes?'

Ruth answered. 'Hot, yes, and beautiful in places.'

'Maybe I come visit you one day?'

Abi and Ann looked at each other. 'Perhaps you will, but we don't even know your name yet.'

'Ahh, yes my name it is Ahmet.'

That makes it alright then, thought Ann. *He can come visit now.*

'Ahmet is a very nice name.' said Ruth, and the two continued their little tête-à-tête while Ann and Abi looked on. Within about forty minutes Ruth knew practically all she needed to know about Ahmet and he knew practically all the details of their lives in the Emirates.

'I hate to break up this little party,' said Ann, pointedly, 'but we do need to be making a move soon.'

'Oh OK.' said Ruth. 'Anyway, it's been nice getting to know you, Ahmet. Maybe we will see you again before we leave.'

'I hope so Madam Ruth and maybe you will think about adopting me, yes?' He took her hand and kissed the back of it.

I don't bloody think so! thought Abi *I can imagine what Toufiq would have to say about that.*

'Are you for real?' asked Ann when they got outside 'What was all that about?'

'I felt sorry for him,' said Ruth, 'So I said if he ever made it to Dubai he could come visit me.'

'So where did the adoption bit come from?' Ann enquired.

'I think he might have misunderstood when I said I wished I had a son like him, jokingly saying I would adopt him if I could.'

'Oh, my days. Unbelievable.' Ann was suitably unimpressed.

'I think we better blindfold and gag you for the rest of the week, before you get us into any more bloody trouble,' Abi chipped in.

'I was only joking.'

'Pfft!' Abi responded. 'Anyway, what are we doing now? It's gone eight o'clock and I'm shattered.'

'I say we head back to the hotel and have a nice quiet drink in the bar,' suggested Ann.

'That sounds like a plan,' Ruth agreed. 'Let's grab a cab.'

Returning to the main drag they headed back towards Taksim Square itself, where they found a taxi quite easily and were soon on their way.

Back at the hotel, they headed first to the reception to check whether there was any news on Ruth's passport, which there wasn't, so they went into the bar. It was busy but not overly so and they grabbed a table near to a heat source to try to warm up a little. They still hadn't acclimatised to the cold.

'Ok so what's everyone having?' asked Ann. None of them were particularly big drinkers, but they were on holiday and for once, irresponsible

'Let's go mad and have a cocktail,' Ruth looked hopeful. 'Please?'

'Cocktails? Since when do you drink cocktails? Are you sure? You're such a lightweight when it comes to alcohol,' Abi looked at her.

'Hark who's talking,' said Ann. 'One Black Russian and you're wasted.'

'Your point being?' Abi asked. 'I'm on holiday, I don't have to worry about the kids, or getting up early in the morning for anything. In fact, basically, there's nothing I have to worry about. So yes, I'm up for it.'

'OK fair enough, but don't say I didn't warn you. Can I please suggest, before we go down that road, that we have a think about what we're doing tomorrow? Whatever it is we've got to go to the airport first.'

'You had to go and spoil it didn't you,' Abi was not looking happy.

'I'm only saying.'

'All right, but don't.'

At this point, Ruth interrupted. 'That's tomorrow. Tonight, I'm going to have a Daiquiri, so there, do with that what you will.'

'Oooooh. Get you, missy.'

'I'll have one of those too,' said Abi, determined to enjoy herself.

'OK. Three Daiquiris it is then,' Ann called the waiter over and ordered. The drinks arrived quickly and all three took quite long sips.

'Nice. Always wanted to try one of these,' Ruth looked happy.

'I don't think I've ever had one either,' said Ann.

Abi was no longer looking quite so smug. 'You mean neither of you has had one of these before?' she asked.

'Nope!'

'Nope!'

Oh dear, this isn't going to turn out in a good way she thought.

It didn't take too long before all three had downed them and were ordering seconds. Now, one straight-up Daiquiri is around 40 proof, so one or two shouldn't have too much of an effect, but one too many can easily sneak up on you.

'Look at her over there,' said Abi after her second 'She's definitely suspicious. The one with the shaved head, one dreadlock, and weird clothes. That has got to be some sort of disguise.'

'Where?' asked Ann looking about her.

'Don't start this again you two.'

But they did, and by the end of the evening, according to Ann and Abi, practically everyone in the bar had a secret life of mystery, intrigue, and suspicious activity. Ruth was in despair, but Ann and Abi were, once again, giggling like schoolgirls, pleased with their efforts for the evening.

'OK, enough now,' said Ruth. 'If we're going to do anything tomorrow we should think about getting upstairs.'

'Party pooper,' cried Ann.

'Boo,' joined in Abi.

'You're the one that wanted a cocktail in the first place,' Ann scowled at Ruth.

So, they had a third!

Finally, they stood up and went, a little unsteadily, towards the reception area, after Ruth suggested they asked for recommendations as to somewhere to go the next day. Deniz was on duty and suggested a day trip to Bursa if they wanted to get out of Istanbul. It would involve a coach trip, a boat trip, and a cable car ride and would take them all day. So they booked it there and then, getting all the details they needed, in writing, as none of them would remember the next day. As they headed towards the lift Abi turned back and said to Deniz, 'I don't think the staff here are very happy with us are they?' Ann and Ruth were suitably horrified.

'Madam, why would we not be happy with you? You are our guests and we are here to serve you.'

'Because we've been nothing but a pain since we arrived and are always bothering you.'

'No, no Madam. This is not so.'

Ann was trying desperately to drag Abi away before she said something that would definitely upset the staff.

They called the lift and Ann unceremoniously shoved Abi in, but before the doors closed a *very* handsome, well dressed, olive-skinned man, also got in and stood right next to Ann, who promptly slid, very slowly and quite deliberately, down the wall of the lift as if in a faint, flickering her eyes and holding her chest as she grinned at Ruth opposite. Abi looked from her to the stranger and in broken English declared 'She needs her medicine,' using her hands to indicate that Ann was, perhaps, a little bit unstable.

Whether he needed to or not they didn't know, but the good-looking man got out very quickly on the next floor.

'What the hell are you doing?' asked Ruth.

'I'm sorry but I couldn't help it. He was sooo gorgeous looking.'

'Honestly, can't take you anywhere.'

They all burst out laughing as the doors closed behind him.

Now knowing what their plans for tomorrow were, they started to get changed for bed as soon as they were back in their room, feeling tired after the long day they had had. As they were about to get into bed the phone rang. 'Who the hell is that? asked Ruth. 'It can't be Toufiq, it's way too late.'

Abi, being nearest, answered the phone. 'Hello. Oh hello, yes…Oh, that's very good of you to let us know. Thank you very much.'

Ann and Ruth looked at her expectantly.

'That was Deniz,' she said. 'He wanted to let us know that he has asked all the staff and they all like us very much and are calling us 'The Golden Girls' but was quick to point out that it's not in age but attitude!'

Chapter 8

Bursa

In spite of the alcohol of the night before, Ann, Ruth, and even Abi were awake and out of bed first thing, maybe down to the time difference, excited at the thought of the day ahead and what it might bring.

They grabbed a quick drink in their room, and, as Ann had been up first and was ready to go, with her coat on, she took hers out onto the balcony despite the cold air. Still being very early, there was no major growl of passing traffic, only the occasional car or bus, and that smell of petrol and diesel she had found quite overwhelming when they first arrived, was not yet apparent in the air. She glanced across the still dark street to where the lights of McDonald's showed it was open and was already busy. The thought of a McMuffin flashed through her mind but she quickly dismissed it, and was looking forward to breakfast in the hotel's restaurant, which should be open in around fifteen minutes.

They had planned to get a cab to the airport immediately after breakfast to do the daily report. Ann was hoping they didn't have to send out the search parties again for Ruth and that she would find her way to the exit easily today, as they needed to be back at the hotel no later than nine-thirty to catch the coach. This would then collect passengers from a number of other hotels locally and deposit them at the Yenikapi terminal to catch the ferry at ten-thirty.

Once Abi and Ruth were ready, they all went down to the restaurant and ate the usual breakfast mezze, piling their plates higher than normal as they weren't too sure when their next meal would be. They had already arranged for a taxi to collect them at seven-thirty and they were assured this would give them plenty of time for the airport run.

For once everything went smoothly (little did they know what was to come later in the day) and they were back at the hotel a few minutes after nine. They sat in the reception area and had another hot drink while they waited and right on time the coach pulled up in front of the hotel.

Only two people from their hotel boarded with them, but there were already several people from different hotels seated on the coach. They headed towards the rear and were able to sit together on the bench seat at the back.

'Hey, this is alright isn't it?' quipped Abi, taking her seat. 'And I get to sit by the window.'

'You and your bloody window seat obsession,' said Ann. 'What is it with you and window seats?'

'I really don't like being squashed in the middle,' Abi retorted. 'Makes me claustrophobic.'

'Don't start you two,' said Ruth, frowning. 'Let's have a nice, quiet, normal day shall we.'

Huh, fat chance! When these three got together there was *always* trouble of one kind or another.

The coach travelled around the different areas to the other hotels, collecting passengers en-route. Several of the streets were extremely narrow, leaving very little room for the large coach to manoeuvre the tight bends, but the driver expertly managed them. It was a hair-raising experience and they were glad once all the passengers had been collected and they were heading towards the ferry terminal. They arrived in plenty of time for the ferry, which was ready and waiting for everyone to board.

'How long's the crossing?' asked Ruth.

'I think it's about two hours, maybe a little more,' said Ann. 'I hope neither of you two gets seasick.'

'Not me,' said Abi.

'Nor me,' said Ruth.

Thank the lord for small mercies, thought Ann, *one less thing to worry about.*

People were milling about but the friends headed inside to find a seat before it filled up. They didn't fancy being outside as it was frosty anyway but once on the open water, they knew it would feel a hell of a lot chillier. The seating was typically basic, being more wooden bench than armchair swish, but there was a refreshment bar and a sign for toilets so all was looking good. Once again Abi had managed to grab a window seat.

Within minutes they heard the rumble of the engines and felt the boat (for it was a boat, not a ship) swaying on the water. Luckily it wasn't too choppy so they settled in for the journey.

After about half an hour, Ann announced she was going to go out on deck. Every summer, when she was a little girl, she had taken the ferry with her parents across the Irish Sea, from Fishguard to Rosslare, and she had always adored being outside for at least part of her journey, so that she could smell the brininess of the sea, feel the whip of the wind in her hair, and sometimes the spray of water on her face.

'Are you completely bonkers?' asked Ruth. 'You'll freeze to death out there.'

'I'll be fine. I won't stay outside too long. I like being out on the open water and it will proper wake me up.'

'Rather you than me,' said Abi. 'I'm staying put where it's warm and dry. I can see as much from in here thank you very much.'

'Don't know what you're missing,' Ann shouted back over her shoulder as she made her way outside.

Bliss, she thought, *as she held onto the handrail* (or taffrail to give it its proper title). *You can almost taste the sea. Love it!* She watched the shoreline disappear from view as she stood at the rear of the boat (she found out long ago that it's best to stand there if you're outside, as its more stable and less rocky than the bow of a ship.) *I wish it was a little bit warmer, I could happily stay out here till we get to the other side then.* But it wasn't, so she couldn't and after about thirty minutes she made her way back inside.

'Bloody hell! You look frozen,' cried Ruth, looking at Ann's windswept hair and ruddy cheeks.

Ann suddenly noticed the little man kneeling on the floor in front of Ruth, polishing her Mary Poppins boots. 'Nah. I'm fine. Bracing is the word. Bracing!' she said. 'Errm…what's going on here?'

'Can't you tell? We're having our boots cleaned,' said Abi looking very slightly suspicious.

Ann took her seat and watched as the boot man proceeded to clean her friend's boots to a high shine. Abi had obviously already had hers done, as you could almost see your face in them. As he finished Ruth's he moved across to kneel in front of her.

'No. No. I don't want mine cleaned,' she cried, as Abi and Ruth laughed hysterically, watching as the boot man started applying polish to her boots. 'Tell him to stop. Get him off,' she cried frantically.

But whatever she said he obviously didn't understand and simply carried on polishing her **suede** boots. With Ruth and Abi almost crying with laughter by now.

'I'm going to kill you two. I suppose you think this is funny. Do you know what… you two can pay for a new pair before we go home. And you can pay him for "*polishing*" them too.'

'Worth every penny just to see the look of horror on your face,' said Ruth.

Abi said nothing, she couldn't, as she was almost hysterical with laughter.

'Friends like you who needs enemies?' Ann got in one last comment as the boot man finished his job.

Apart from this incident, the journey across the Marmara Sea was uneventful and actually quite smooth, and by the time they reached the other side and the ferry terminal in Yalova, Ann had calmed down.

Disembarking, they quickly found their coach and boarded for the final stage of their journey to Bursa, another hour or so away. Yet again Abi managed to grab the rear bench seat. The sun was very bright as it reflected off the water, and in the distance they could see the land glistening white from recent snowfalls. As they passed through various little villages along the route they could tell that it had snowed quite heavily, as it still lay deep in places but luckily the roads, which were quite steep, narrow, and serpentine, had been cleared quite effectively.

All three were feeling a little sleepy, but none of them wanted to shut their eyes and miss any of the beautiful countryside they were passing through. They were now on the Asian side of the Marmara Sea and the landscape was quite different to the European side, more typically Turkish and old-worldly, looking almost picture-perfect in places. Yalova itself looked like an interesting city, but they wouldn't have time to explore it today.

'Wow! Isn't it beautiful?' said Ann, who was taking in as much as she could from her side of the coach. 'Don't like the look of the drop though, it's a long way down from here.'

'Yes, fantastic,' said Ruth. 'I'm so glad we decided to come today and we're not even in Bursa yet.'

'Shame we'll only have a few hours to explore the summit today. Bursa itself is meant to be full of historical places dating right back to the Ottoman Empire,' Ann answered.

'Yes, that is a shame,' said Abi. 'You know what I'm like with my history and historical places.'

'You better make the most of it, because I very much doubt we'll be allowed to come here again after this trip, especially on our own.'

'Oh, go on. Rub it in,' said Ruth 'Will I ever live this down?'

'Nope!'

'Nope! So, you've now got two claims to fame in Istanbul. Eh?' quipped Abi.

Arriving in the city of Bursa, the three friends exited the coach and were immediately mesmerised by the hustle and bustle of the central bazaar and the surrounding streets. As they waited to be told where to go next, they were spying out places to shop, and plotting as to how they might actually be able to squeeze a couple in before they had to head back to the boat later on.

'I don't know what I expected, but it wasn't this,' said Ann.

'No, and look at the mountain, I didn't realise it was so high. It looks stunning,' replied Abi

Ruth was about to wander off and Ann caught her arm just in time. 'Where do you think you're going?' she asked.

'I was only going to have a little wander to see what's here,' pleaded Ruth.

'No, you're not,' said Abi. 'If one goes we all go. Not having you getting lost here so we have to come looking for you.'

'Spoilsport!'

Honestly, what are we going to do with her? thought Ann.

'If we have time we'll take a look later, but I think at the moment the tour guide is trying to get us on to the Teleferik (cable car) so come on.'

'You mean the gour tide?' laughed Ruth.

'Again with the gour tide?' said Abi.

'Well, maybe she works the same way you do?' Ruth smirked.

Ann and Abi looked at each other without speaking.

'Come ladies, this way,' said the *gour tide,* pointing towards the cable car entrance.

'Oh my god! This is going to take hours,' said Abi, looking at the queue as it snaked its way around the barriers inside the building.

Not only was the cable car used to ferry tourists to the top it was also used to take groups of skiers up, and there were plenty of them in the queue.

'We could be forever,' cried Ruth who was not normally prone to exaggeration.

'We don't have a choice,' said Ann.

'I think we might have,' said Ruth as she walked back towards Zehra, the tour guide.

Keeping her eyes very firmly on Ruth, Ann said, 'What's she up to now?'

'Your guess is as good as mine,' said Abi.

A couple of minutes later Ruth came back with Zehra in tow. 'Zehra has very kindly offered to wait in the queue for us while we go to buy some water. I've explained that we haven't had a drink for a long while and are very thirsty. She says there's a shop a little way down the road where we can buy it,' Ruth winked as she spoke.

'Thank you very much, very kind of you,' said Ann.

Abi stood with her mouth open.

They left Zehra to guard their spot and once outside Abi spluttered 'You didn't…'

'Didn't what?' laughed Ruth. 'She won't mind, she'll only be hanging around outside herding people otherwise. At least in here, she'll be warm.'

'I don't believe you did that!' Ann was gobsmacked.

'Okay, but listen, if we stand here arguing the toss for the next half an hour and don't go now and have a mooch around, we'll run out of time anyway. So move it.'

They headed off down the road following the signs for the Central Bazaar, which was reminiscent of the one in Istanbul. There was no way they would get around all of it as it was a labyrinth of covered market streets, shops, and storage warehouses.

They decided to stick to the two-storey caravanserais known as the Koza Han. It was originally built as a 'guest house' around a central courtyard, to provide a safe resting place for traders and their caravans (*where the name caravanserais originates*) against the elements and the risk of robbery on the road. Such places were very common along the route of the Silk Road, on which Bursa was once a major stop, but it now housed many stores specialising in silk and silk products.

'Wow! This is fantastic. You can almost sense the traders with their wares, feel the history of the place,' Abi gushed.

'Maybe, but unfortunately, we don't have time to meander Professor! We need to get a move on,' said Ruth.

They didn't spend too long looking around, as Ann, feeling quite guilty about Zehra, kept pushing them to hurry. Abi still managed to buy herself a pure silk scarf though.

Before long they were heading back up towards the Teleferik when Ann piped up 'Bugger!'

'What? What?' said Ruth

'Water... Water. We need to buy water.'

'Oh yes, I suppose we should.'

By the time they got back, the queue had not grown any less but Zehra had moved forward quite a bit, unfortunately, the crowd was, let's say, reluctant to let them through.

'We're with her,' Abi pointed, in an effort to push through the queue of people.

'Thank you so much again,' said Ann, when they finally reached Zehra. 'We bought you some water too,' she smiled sweetly.

'No need madam but thank you,' Zehra took her leave.

'Good thinking Batman.'

'Shut up Abi. It was the least we could do. Now can we settle down? Hopefully, we'll be on our way to the top soon.'

'How long does it take?' asked Ruth.

'Hmmm? As it's the world's longest cable car, quite a while I should think.' said Ann.

'What? The longest? How do you know that?' asked Abi.

Ann took a little book out of her bag. 'From this,' she said holding up a tourist guide.

'When did you buy that?'

'I got it before we came. Thought it might be useful.'

'Smarty Pants.'

'It says here,' Ann countered, '"The Bursa Teleferik travels up the side of the mountain, swooping over thickly forested lower slopes. From one side you can see the jagged mountain peak and from the other, you can look down on the city of Bursa below. The ride covers approximately eight point two kilometres and it takes roughly twenty-two minutes to reach the top!" So there! Anything else you want to know?'

'Do I have to go?' Ruth asked, suddenly going pale.

'What do you mean do you have to go? Of course you bloody have to go. It's the whole point of coming here. Why what's wrong?' Abi asked.

'I don't like heights!'

'Clearly, now's not a very good time to tell us *that*.'

'It's ok,' said Ann. 'I'm sure Abi won't mind lending you her new scarf so we can blindfold you. That way you won't know how high we are.'

'Yeah right! Like that's going to happen,' Abi said indignantly.

'Don't be mean.'

'I'll definitely have to keep my eyes closed,' offered Ruth.

The crowd moved slowly on and after fifteen minutes or so they were boarding. Actually, Abi was dragging, and Ann was pushing Ruth into the cable car cabin.

'Look, there's a seat there, at the back. If we sit on that, if you faint at least we won't have to peel you up off the floor,' Abi said.

'Good idea,' said Ann, as she continued to push Ruth further into the cabin towards the bench seat. 'Keep your eyes facing forward and whatever you do DON'T look down.'

Ruth had turned visibly paler and sat rigidly on the seat, eyes firmly facing front and focusing on the people ahead of her. 'Here, take this,' said Ann handing her a large paper bag. 'What's this for?' Ruth asked.

'Just in case, Ruth, just in case.'

Slowly, the cable car began to rise, climbing steadily towards the summit. Everyone, apart from Ruth that is, who had her eyes tight shut, were *oohing* and *aahing* at the scenery. Ahead, the snow-capped peak was clearly visible and on one side the tops of the trees were sprinkled with a thin white dusting of snow and on the other, the city of Bursa sprawled out below.

'Beautiful,' said Ann dreamily. 'It's like a scene from a picture postcard.'

'Oh please!' said Abi. 'Enough with the romantic claptrap. Yes, it's nice but give it another couple of months and it'll be grey and slushy and not beautiful at all.'

'I don't want any descriptions of how high up we are,' said Ruth. 'Please keep the height out of it.'

'Wuss.'

'Oh my god! Do we have to come down the same way?' Ruth asked anxiously. 'I don't think I can do this twice in one day.'

'Nooo,' said Ann. 'I'm sure we can arrange a pair of skis for you. We'll simply give you a push and away you'll go.'

'Stop it! That's not funny.'

'Honestly! I think we go back down by coach so stop panicking. Besides which it will be dark by then so you wouldn't see anything anyway.' As she said this Ann had her fingers firmly crossed behind her back.

Abi was way too distracted to join in this particular dialogue, deep in conversation about the merits of this mode of travel with a couple of backpackers.

Ruth went quiet, and having taken the plunge and finally opened her eyes again, was concentrating very hard on only looking upwards, toward the summit.

Abi had finished her conversation with the backpackers and was again taking in the scenery. 'Oooh look,' she said, 'those people down there look like teeny weeny ants.'

'Abi, stop it,' Ann said.

'What? I didn't mention height!'

'No, but the phrase "*teeny weeny ants*" sort of gives it away.'

Taking in the scenery, talking to random strangers, along with winding up Ruth, the journey to the summit seemed to pass very quickly.

Around twenty minutes later they arrived at the final station of the Teleferik, some eighteen-hundred and ten metres above sea level.

Stepping out onto the platform, the cold, crisp air greeted them. Being used to the sultry, humid air of the Emirates, they all breathed in deeply, enjoying the smell, taste, and feel of the clean air that they could only experience in Dubai if they travelled high up into the mountains such as Jebel Hafeet or Hatta, which didn't happen too often.

'Oh wow! How beautiful is this?' Ruth exclaimed.

'Worth the journey then?' asked Ann.

'Definitely.'

Abi meantime was looking all around her, the snow-covered peak was filled with people, some milling around, others heading to the ski resort, others who had come in their party on the coach huddled together, waiting for the '*gour tide*' to fill them in on what happened next.

The views were breathtaking. Yes, it was cold, but for now, the sun was out and the blindingly white snow glistened all around. Not far away stood what were obviously ski chalets. There were also a few shops and restaurants, and close by, a big round structure housed what appeared to be a barbeque area.

The '*gour tide*' told them they had around 3 hours to freely wander, but to stay away from the ski areas. The barbeque would be ready within thirty minutes and was included in their tour package. She pointed out where they would all meet up at the end of the day and confirmed, due to road conditions, they would be returning to the lower level by cable car. From there the coach would take them the rest of the way down the mountain pass and to the ferry, and then onward to Istanbul.

'You lied,' cried Ruth. 'You said we were going back by coach.'

'We are,' said Ann. 'Only not all the way. You'll be fine and it'll be dark by then.'

'Not happy,' said Ruth.

'Wuss,' said Abi (again).

They decided to have a little meander around until it was time for the barbeque. Unfortunately, Ruth's Mary Poppins boots turned out not to be the best footwear to have on, as she was slipping and sliding all over the place. Several times, either Abi or Ann, had to rescue her before she fell, and at one point a man who was passing, also had to reach out to steady her, which was embarrassing enough. However, when he looked at Ruth, and then towards Ann and Abi, and without blinking said, 'Aaaah! You are English ladies no passport, yes?' They all wanted the ground to open up and swallow them. He definitely wasn't from their hotel, so they were a bit confused about how he knew. But they soon learnt that nearly everyone, in every hotel local to theirs, also knew. Which of course meant that most of the people on today's trip would know too.

Ann was the first to respond. 'Yes. It seems our friend somehow managed to pick up the wrong passport in her rush to get to the airport and we didn't realise until we reached Istanbul,' she was very quick to place the blame firmly on Ruth, who by now was going all sorts of red.

'This is what we heard,' he replied. 'But we couldn't believe it could happen this way.'

'I can confirm it definitely did,' said Abi, also distancing herself from any blame. 'We are hoping our friend's husband can get the right passport to her before we have to travel again on Friday.'

'Can happen to anyone,' Ruth said, wilting under the glares from the others.

Abi, in her usual unique fashion, was soon deep in conversation with the man and found out he was indeed one of their coach party, that he and his family were from Kuwait, who were staying at a hotel very close to their own and had heard about the friends from other people in their hotel.

Eventually, the man and his family left to do their own meandering. Ruth was standing apart from the group, trying to look inconspicuous but not succeeding, as every time she tried to move away her feet refused to go in the same direction as each other, so in the end, she just stood very, very still.

'So that's it then,' said Abi. 'From now on, everywhere we go, we'll be known as "*English lady, no passport.*" Sort of explains some of the funny looks we've been getting today.'

'It's not my fault.'

'Well if it's not your fault, whose is it?'

'Someone at home must have moved the passports.'

'That may be but since when did you become colour-blind?'

'I'm not.'

'I rest my case!'

'Come on you two. Enough with the bickering. Barbecue's ready and I'm starving now. Let's go eat and then are free to wander,' said Ann.

Linking arms, with Ruth in between them, they headed towards the food. The smell was making them ravenous but it was slow going as the ground was quite slippery, even in the right footwear.

The food was plentiful and delicious, with a mix of chicken and lamb kebabs and salad, wrapped in locally made Turkish flatbread, served with either apple or mint tea.

'Delicious,' from Ann.

'Yep,' from Abi.

'I sooo needed this,' said Ruth, who had managed to stay upright by holding her food in one hand and gripping the edge of the serving area with the other. 'I'm going to need the loo after this though before I can go walkabout.'

'It's over there,' said Ann, pointing. 'Try walking and not slinking and you might actually make it on your own.'

'Harsh!' and with that off she went, stepping heavily and placing her feet very carefully in an effort to stay standing.

Ann and Abi watched in amusement. 'Come on, let's wait over here for her,' Abi suggested.

They found a bench to sit on whilst they finished their warming drinks, leisurely taking in the sights and sounds around them.

'Wonder if there's any sign of the passport yet?' said Ann

'Maybe. If Toufiq was able to send it yesterday, it might, I say might, get to the hotel by the time we get back tonight, but I'm not holding my breath.'

'Be good though if it did, at least then we know we'll be ok to fly on Friday night, and we can spend some more time sightseeing, instead of hiking off to the airport again and spending the day worrying whether it will arrive in time.'

'Well, we'll have to wait and see.'

They both lapsed into silence, lost in thought about what they would do if it didn't arrive in time and almost as important and worrying, was the fact that Ruth's visa was due to run out the next day, which could mean, when they arrived at the airport in the morning, detention or deportation. So engrossed were they in their thoughts, they didn't notice the time passing.

'Thanks a bunch, you two,' Ruth's voice reached them, sounding quite stressed.

'What? What's up?' said Abi

'What's up? I'll tell you what's up. I've been stuck in the bloody loo for the last half an hour and did either of you notice, or come to look for me? No.'

'Ooops!' said Ann. 'We've only been sat here enjoying the scenery and didn't notice the time.'

'How the hell did you manage to lock yourself in you dingbat?'

'I didn't *lock myself* in. The door jammed, and the lock jammed, and I couldn't get out. Nobody else came in for ages and when they did they didn't speak English, so my crying *"Help! I'm locked in,"* sort of fell on deaf ears. The door was too low to crawl under and too high to climb over so I was stuck.'

'Why always you?' asked Ann. 'Why is it always you that ends up in chaos?'

'It isn't *always* me,' said Ruth.

'Errh… I think you'll find it is,' said Abi.

'If you were proper friends you would have noticed I'd been a long time and come to find me.'

'So how did you manage to get out in the end?' asked Ann, a slight grin on her face, wondering what was coming next.

'I kept on calling for help, and then tried waving under the door when I heard someone come in, and finally, a lady noticed and went for help. Never been so embarrassed.'

Ann and Abi looked at each other and then at her. 'Really?' they said in unison.

'Stuff just happens to me,' Ruth exclaimed.

'We'd noticed,' countered Ann.

'OK. OK. Let's go for a wander around, we don't have a great deal of time left now and I want to see what else is here before we have to leave. There are a few shops over there,' said Abi, pointing to the few buildings that were visible.

'I don't especially want to go shopping,' said Ruth. 'I'll stay here and wait for you.'

'Err... I don't think so,' said Ann. 'Where we go, you go. Not letting you out of our sight again today, otherwise, god knows what else might happen.'

The shops turned out to be the usual sort of touristy places you expect to find in any popular holiday spots, which Bursa definitely was, so they actually didn't spend very much time in them at all.

'That was a bit disappointing,' said Abi.

'What were you expecting? Balenciaga? Chanel? Dior?' asked Ann.

'No,' countered Abi. 'Only a little more than there was.'

'It's a tourist destination, at the top of a bloody mountain!'

'I know that but…'

'But what? You have high expectations of wilderness destinations then?'

'You're being nasty now.'

'No, I'm not, but it was obviously either going to be a souvenir emporium or a skiers paradise. Not an outlet for haute couture.'

'Really thought there'd be a bit more,' Abi said awkwardly.

'Shopaholic!' replied Ann. 'Anyway, we need to start making our way back now. We'll be leaving in about 15 minutes. It'll take us a bit longer now; it's getting quite dark.'

Slowly, they made their way back to the top of the Teleferik, Ruth looking more and more anxious the closer they got.

'Is there honestly no other way down?' she asked.

'Look, I offered to put you on a pair of skis and give you a push but you didn't like that idea. So no, there is no other way down. You won't notice how high up we are now, it's way too dark to see anything,' Ann said.

'Did you have to mention *how high up?*'

'Listen, do what you did on the way up, sit at the back and keep your eyes shut,' said Abi. 'You'll be fine.'

Night was fast descending, the light fading very quickly, and many of those who had come up earlier had either gone to the ski resort or left already, so the queue was nowhere near as long and they were soon in the cable car and settled, with Ruth again sitting, eyes shut tight.

'Doesn't know what she's missing,' Abi said to Ann, glancing back at Ruth.

'Oh leave her be. We'll be down before she knows it and we can enjoy the twinkly lights of Bursa in the distance.'

'You're being mushy again.'

'Oh shut up! Go find someone else to talk to and let me enjoy the scenery, what we can see of it.'

'I will,' she said. 'Mr. Kuwait is over there. I want to try and find out exactly how he knew about us.' And off she went.

The cable car was hushed. Everyone, apart from Ruth that is, was looking out over the vista before them and to either side. There wasn't very much to see but Ann thought it was beautiful anyway.

As they were coming into the Teleferik station at the lowest of the levels Ann went back to Ruth.

'Oi! We're nearly at the bottom now so you can open your eyes.'

'Never again! said Ruth 'Never again!'

Exiting the Telefrik area, their coach was waiting for them across the road so they headed straight for it, looking forward to some warmth and a comfortable journey back to the ferry.

'Bloody hell. Did you see that?' said Abi, as they took their seats at the back of the coach.

'What?' asked Ann.

'The driver. He's got two full cases of full-fat coke by the side of his seat!'

'Maybe some of them are for the passengers?' Ann said.

'I hope so, otherwise, he's going to be as high as a kite by the time we get to the ferry, never mind what he'll be like by the time we reach the hotel.'

Ruth appeared oblivious to both the conversation and the topic of it.

'Let's wait and see,' said Ann, silently praying to the powers that be.

'Wait and see what?' Ruth finally joined in.

'Nothing. We were only talking about how long the journey will take,' lied Abi. *Best not to let her know, she'll only start panicking,* she thought.

They started off calmly enough, snaking downwards through the narrow streets but at a leisurely pace. Once they got out on the open road it was a different story. They were now at a much lower level, but they were still, essentially, travelling down the side of a mountain, only the driver appeared to have forgotten this and before very long the coach felt like it was hurtling towards hell. They hadn't taken too much notice of the roads on the way up to Bursa as they had been occupied taking in the scenery, but now they realised that not only were the roads very narrow, but they also snaked their way *around* the mountain, with the rock face on one side and oblivion on the other.

'Any money he's already downed at least one case of coke,' Ann ventured, forgetting that Ruth hadn't noticed the cases by the driver's seat.

'I think you're right. He's a bloody lunatic!' agreed Abi.

'Oh my God! He's going to get us all killed,' Ruth sounded worried.

'What's the speed limit on this road? Can't be more than forty km an hour can it?' asked Ann.

'He sure ain't sticking to it, even if it's seventy-five.'

'I want to get off,' said Ruth.

'Good luck with that,' said Ann.

To say that the journey back to the ferry was hair raising would be slightly under egging it. Almost from the moment they left the city limits and started down the road towards the ferry port at Yalova, the coach careered left and right, coming perilously close to the edge and the yawning blackness beyond, scraping tree branches as it went, way over the speed limit and with the driver, who, if he wasn't puffing on yet another cigarette, was singularly putting away more Coke than the entire passenger list on a good night at a rave.

'I think I'm gonna be sick,' cried Ruth.

'Well don't. Hold on, we can't be too far from the ferry now,' said Ann.

'Don't know what your problem is,' said Abi. 'Really, it's just like being on a rollercoaster at the fair.'

'I don't know what fairgrounds you go to,' said Ann. 'Ruth is looking pretty green around the gills.'

'She's fine. Don't pander to her histrionics.'

'I am NOT being histrionic!'

'Here, take this,' said Abi, passing her another paper bag she'd found in the seat pocket. 'This'll have to do for now but I would prefer it if you could desist from chucking up until we're off the coach.'

'I'll try,' said Ruth through gritted teeth.

'Finally,' said Ann, as the coach reached more level ground and the driver slowed a little. 'Look, over there. It's the ferry.'

For the second time that day, Ruth repeated, 'Never again! Never again!'

Without exception, the passengers unsteadily got off the coach and began making their way towards the ferry, some appearing to share Ruth's version of the journey, looking slightly greenish and others erring on the side of Abi, not exactly laughing but certainly not looking worried in any way.

Go figure, thought Ann, *how can all these people have experienced that journey so differently?* Looking at Ruth she said, 'If Abi ever asks us to go to a funfair with her please remind me to say a very firm NO.'

'Don't worry, after that journey, I never want to see a roller coaster again.'

'What's your problem?' asked Abi, grinning.

It didn't take long to board the ferry and they were soon inside, sitting quietly and feeling warmer and safer. There was nothing to see apart from lights in the distance and with the gentle swaying of the boat Ann and Ruth had soon dozed off.

'Typical,' said Abi to no one. 'I honestly don't know how they do it.'

She soon found another random stranger to chat to, to break up the monotony of the crossing.

Because Ann and Ruth slept most of the way, and Abi was busy gossiping with anyone who would listen, this part of the journey seemed to pass very quickly and they were soon back on terra firma.

The '*gour tide*', who had travelled on a different coach to theirs, was waiting for them by the final coach that would take them back to their hotels. 'Good evening everyone, did you all have a good day?'

'Don't,' said Abi, grabbing Ann's arm as she opened her mouth to say something. 'We're here, we're safe. What's the point?'

Ann looked at her in disbelief. 'Are you serious? That head case could have killed us all.'

'Don't exaggerate. He simply had a need for speed. Vroom, vroom!'

Looking at them in horror, Ruth gave a strangled cry. 'No, no, no, no, no!'.

As they glanced into the coach they noticed the same driver, complete with his remaining crate of coke, seated behind the wheel.

'It's fine,' said Abi. 'At least there's no edge to go over this time.'

'No, only the one Ruth's about to go over,' replied Ann. 'But at least he won't be able to speed too much around these streets.'

That remained to be seen.

Taking their preferred seat at the back of the coach, Ann pulled a couple of snack bars from her bag. 'Anyone want one of these?' she asked, 'Or these?' As she produced two small bottles of water.

'What the hell? Where did they come from?' asked Abi. 'What sort of bag is that? It's like one of those magicians bags, endless contents appearing out of nowhere.'

'Leave my bag alone. It's not a magician's bag, it's that I'm good at packing it properly to get more in,' said Ann defensively.

'I'll have a water if I can please,' said Ruth. 'I don't think I could stomach eating anything right now.'

'Fair enough,' said Ann, handing her one of the bottles.

'You?' looking at Abi.

'No, you're alright. I'll have a coffee when we get back to the hotel.'

The coach pulled out of the ferry car park and began the process of dropping people at their respective hotels, the first of which was along the main road facing the water, so the roads were quite wide, well-lit, and reasonably straight. The driver then turned up towards the older part of Istanbul where the streets became narrower but were still just wide enough to pass safely. After about forty-five minutes there were only a handful of people left.

'That wasn't bad was it?' said Ann.

'Suppose not,' said Ruth. 'I'll be glad to get off, he's still knocking back the coke and chain-smoking.'

'Not long to go now.'

The coach stopped at a hotel and the remaining passengers got off.

'Oh shit!' said Ann. 'That's not good. We're the only ones left. He must have taken a different route, because we weren't the first to get on. I don't know where the other two are that got on with us.' She looked at Ruth, who in turn looked at Abi in dismay.

'Listen, what's the worst that could happen?' said Abi. 'We'll be fine. We can't be that far from the hotel now.'

With that, the driver took a wide turn to the left and started to climb what appeared to be a very steep, very narrow, poorly lit road.

'Christ! How's he gonna get up there?' said Ann, looking out of the window. 'You couldn't get a fag paper between the side of the coach and the cars parked on this side of the road.'

Ruth's knuckles were white as she gripped the back of the seat in front of her.

They suddenly heard a lot of shouting in Turkish as several men appeared, coming from a pavement café, who then proceeded to make rude signs at the driver, pointing towards the parked cars. They looked less than happy.

'He's never going to make it!' cried Ruth.

'Looks like he's going to give it a bloody good try,' replied Ann.

The men outside seemed to be getting agitated and while they couldn't understand what was being said Abi, Ruth, and Ann knew it wasn't good.

'What if they try and get onto the coach?' asked Ruth.

'They can't, dipstick. The doors can only be opened from the inside by the driver,' said Abi.

'But they might start throwing things.'

'Oh please!' said Abi. 'Don't be such a drama queen.'

Suddenly, the coach came to an abrupt halt. The driver stood up and peered out of the windows on both sides, scratching his head and gesticulating at the men on the pavement.

'What the hell is he doing now?' asked Ann.

'I don't know, but whatever it is I don't like it,' said Ruth.

The driver then opened the window on the side where the men were standing and said something to them. They immediately quietened down and a couple of them started scratching their heads too. One or two slowly walked around to the other side of the coach, pointing and talking to the driver, he nodded and then got back behind the wheel.

'Now what?' said Ann. 'Oh my God no! He can't be serious.'

But it appeared he was, as he put the coach in reverse and started going backward, with the men on either side trying to guide him back down the road and stopping any further traffic from coming up.

'I can't watch,' said Ruth.

'Me either,' agreed Ann.

Abi on the other hand appeared to be in her element. 'This is fun,' she said.

'It's not. If he so much as touches any of these cars we'll all be in deep trouble,' said Ruth.

'Just keep your head down and pray,' said Ann.

Painfully slowly, more or less inch by inch, the coach backed all the way down the street until, at last, it was able to reverse back onto the main road to the cheers and applause of the accompanying group of men.

'I think I might have wet myself,' exclaimed Ruth.

'Nice. Very nice!' said Abi.

They found out later that the coach driver had actually taken a wrong turn.

With no further dramas, they arrived, safely, back at their hotel at about eleven o'clock.

'God, I hope the bar's still open,' said Ann. 'I need a stiff drink.'

'I need a coffee.'

'And I need the loo,' said Ruth. 'Maybe a drink too.'

The bar was still open and so were the loos so within about ten minutes they all had what they needed.

Deniz brought their order across to the table. 'How was your day ladies?' he asked politely.

They looked at each other and now that they were back safe, were warm and comfortable, burst out into uncontrollable giggles. (Probably nerves.)

Deniz was unsure what had just happened, so he simply placed the drinks on the table and went back to the reception desk.

'Crazy English ladies!' he muttered to himself. *'Very crazy English ladies.'*

Ruth had started to raise her glass towards her lips when she heard Deniz calling.. 'Madam…Madam.'

'Oh bloody hell, what now?' she said, glancing towards him to make sure she was the *'Madam'* he was talking to. She was.

'I am so sorry. I forgot to give you this when you came in,' he said, passing her a large envelope. 'It arrived this evening.'

Ann and Abi held their breath as Ruth ripped open the envelope. 'Yes. Yes!' she cried. 'It's my passport. At last, I can relax and enjoy myself. Thank you,' she said to Deniz.

'I would suggest we have another drink,' Ann said. 'But as I know where we're going first thing in the morning I guess we ought to head upstairs.'

'At least I'll be able to sleep soundly tonight,' said Ruth, clutching the envelope tightly to her.

'Thank God for that,' said Abi. 'Next time someone says, *"English lady no passport"* you can wave it in their face,' she laughed.

With that, they finished their drinks, and headed upstairs to their room.

Chapter 9

Mosques, Museums and Men in Camel-Hair Coats

The next morning it was Ruth that was up first, eager to get to the airport to present her passport. 'Come on you two. Chop, chop,' she said loudly.

'What?' said Abi, peering out blearily from under her bed covers. 'What's all the noise for?'

'I want to get to the airport and get this thing sorted,' said Ruth.

'So go,' answered Abi.

'I'm not going on my own. You two will have to come with me, just in case.'

'Just in case what?' said Abi. 'You think they've let you in, set you free for three days, and now, when you've actually got your *proper* passport they're going to arrest you?'

'You never know,' said Ruth.

For once, Ann was still snuggled up in bed. She had no desire to engage in the latest round of *guess the outcome* debate. All she wanted was a cup of tea, breakfast, and a nice, uneventful, day of sightseeing. Fat chance!

'Tone it down you two. You'll wake up the whole floor. I am not moving until I've had my tea, a shower, and breakfast. In that order. Then, when I am human once again, I'll join you both on our favourite trip out,' she said.

'Ok. But please can we get going? This is the first day since we've been here that I can move around without worrying about getting stopped -slash – arrested.'

'Weren't too worried in Taksim the other day, were you?' Abi threw in for good measure.

'That was meant to be a joke,' said Ruth. 'I was only messing.'

Neither of them noticed that Ann had got up and was now sitting in the corner, quietly sipping her tea, still not allowing herself to get dragged into the conversation. It was too early in the morning and yesterday had been a *very* long day.

'Where's my coffee then?' Abi asked, finally noticing Ann.

'Snooze you lose!' answered Ann. 'You two were so deep in conversation I didn't want to interrupt.'

'Selfish,' Abi responded.

'Oh get on with it,' Ruth was now sounding a smidgen stressed.

'I'm going for a shower,' Ann picked up her towel from the chair and headed for the bathroom before anyone could argue, leaving the two of them staring after her.

'Well!' said Abi

'Grow up,' said Ruth. 'Get your coffee down you. I want to be out of here within the next 30 minutes. It's going to be busy on the roads this time of the morning and we don't know how long it will take to get everything sorted.'

'If… we get everything sorted,' Abi whispered under her breath, but Ruth still heard her.

'What do you mean "if"?' she said. 'Why wouldn't we?'

'The way everything else has gone this week I'm not holding my breath that today will be all plain sailing.'

'Oh don't,' Ruth pleaded with her. 'Don't say that.'

Ann emerged from the bathroom. 'Thought you wanted to get going?' she said, looking from one to the other. 'You haven't even made your drinks yet. I'll be ready in less than ten minutes and then I'm going down to breakfast, whether you're ready or not. I'm hungry.'

'Her fault,' muttered Ruth, glancing at Abi.

'Don't you blame me. You're just too bloody sensitive!' Abi flashed her eyes in Ruth's direction.

Ann continued to ignore them both and carried on getting ready. *Don't know what they're bickering about now but they can get on with it.*

Ruth grabbed her things and headed towards the bathroom. 'I'll wait and have a drink when we go down for breakfast,' she said.

'What have you been saying to her?' Ann questioned Abi once Ruth closed the bathroom door. 'You been winding her up again?'

'Me?' said Abi, innocently. 'As if.'

'So you have then. Honestly!'

By the time Ruth emerged from the bathroom, Ann was dressed and ready. 'I'm going down,' she said. 'See you there when you've finished faffing.' And with that, she left the room and headed towards the stairs.

'She thinks I've been winding you up,' said Abi.

'You have,' Ruth replied.

Before they had both showered, dressed, and gone down to the restaurant Ann was already halfway through her breakfast and on her third cup of tea.

'What time do you call this?' she asked. 'And what's that for?' she pointed to the jacket Ruth was carrying.

'It's a leather jacket Toufiq bought me a few years ago when he was here on business. I've ripped it,' she said, showing Ann the tear in the sleeve. 'I want to see if it's possible to get it repaired while we're here. There are several leather factories around the Fatih area so I thought we could have a look before we go to see Hagia Sophia and that later on?'

'Seriously, we've been here four days and you're taking it today?'

'We haven't actually had time before now have we?' Ruth replied.

'We're in bloody Fatih – we could have taken it on Tuesday before we went to Taksim.'

'Never thought.' Ruth answered.

'Whatever, but I wouldn't hold your breath you'll get it back before we leave,' Ann said.

'Right you two. Today's plan of action then is the airport, followed by the leather factory, followed by Hagia Sophia and the Blue Mosque – yes?' asked Abi.

'Sounds about right,' said Ann.

'Ok with me,' said Ruth.

'Good. Then can we get on with it?' Abi said. 'Have you ordered a cab, Ann?'

'No, but I'll go and do that now while you two finish eating.' So off she went.

Thirty minutes later they were, once again, heading, towards the airport.

'Oh, God…' Ruth sighed, 'I hope this all goes OK today.'

'So do we,' said Ann, looking sideways at Abi. 'You have got your passport haven't you?' she laughed.

'Very funny – not!' replied Ruth, checking her bag though, just in case.

When the taxi pulled up outside Atatürk Airport, hopefully for the last time before their flight home, Ruth asked 'Will you two come in with me today? I don't think I can face it on my own.'

'I don't mind, but will they let us?' Ann said.

'We can but try,' Abi added. 'You're like old friends with the security guys now though aren't you, so hopefully, it will be ok.'

They headed towards the security office and Ruth knocked, reluctantly, on the door.

'Gelmek' (Come)

'I hope the girl that speaks English is here today,' Ruth said, opening the door and going into the office, closely followed by Ann and Abi. She breathed a massive sigh of relief when she saw the English-speaking security guard at her desk.

'Ah! Good morning madam. Come, come.'

'Is it alright if my friends come in too?' Ruth asked.

'Yes, yes, no problem.'

Several of the other security officers greeted Ruth with a welcoming nod.

'You're temporary visa expires today, yes? Is there any news of your passport?'

Ruth took her passport out of her bag and placed it on the desk. 'Yes. It arrived last night.'

The security officer picked it up and waved it at her colleagues, at which point the whole office burst into spontaneous applause, some even high-fiving each other. *Weird, but nice* thought Ann.

'Very good. Ok, give me your temporary visa too, as that will now have to be cancelled and we will stamp your passport with a new one.'

Ruth handed everything to her, still not quite believing that the nightmare was about to be over. Ann and Abi stood looking on, with their fingers crossed that nothing else would be wrong, like Ruth's passport being out of date for example.

The English-speaking officer took the paperwork and then disappeared into a back office.

Ruth, Ann, and Abi sat waiting nervously for her to reappear, which she did about fifteen minutes later.

'Excellent Madam. Everything is now in order and you are free to go. There is no need for you to return again,' she said, as she handed Ruth's passport back.

'Until tomorrow,' whispered Ann to Abi.

As they left the office there was another round of head nodding and waving.

Ruth, sounding pleased, said 'Wasn't expecting that.'

'They're probably glad to see the back of you,' Abi replied.

'Right. Let's go grab a cab and get the day started properly. Can't wait to see the Blue Mosque and Hagia Sophia,' said Ann.

They asked the cab driver to drop them near the leather factory in Fatih, located quite close to the train station. This would then be within walking distance of the Sultanahmet Park, where they were intending to go later in the day.

Entering the building they were immediately hit with that unique, rich, heady aroma that only leather can produce. It permeated the whole area.

'Oh wow. I think I'm in heaven,' Ann gushed, looking at the rows and rows of leather jackets and bags. She couldn't wait to get her hands on them.

'Fabulous. Nothing like the smell of leather to get the senses racing,' Ruth agreed.

'Oh please! If you smelt it before it's been treated you'd have something else to say,' Abi burst their bubble.

Ignoring her, Ruth approached an older-looking man, who was working towards the back of the shop area.

'You speak English?' she asked hopefully, smiling at him.

'He doesn't but I do,' answered a much more youthful figure, who suddenly appeared from behind a rail of jackets. 'How can I help?'

Ruth showed him the jacket and explained the problem with the tear that was clearly visible on the sleeve. 'Is it possible to fix this?' she asked.

He took the jacket from her and examined it closely before asking 'Do you mind if I take it and show it to one of my tailors?'

'No. That's fine,' Ruth replied, as he disappeared from view.

'All done?' asked Abi.

'Not yet. He's taken it to show to someone else, one of his tailors. Shouldn't be long.'

Ann, meanwhile, was closely examining a rail of ladies' jackets, touching and stroking them gently. *Oh wow. These are so smooth, so soft, virtually like silk. I bet they'd feel like a second skin to wear. Pure, unadulterated luxury.*

'What are you doing?' Abi enquired.

Ann started, so lost was she in her reverie. 'Nothing. Only looking.'

'Drooling more like.'

'A girl can dream.'

'Why dream, have you seen the prices? They're ridiculously cheap.'

Ann hadn't, she'd been way too busy lusting after the goods to notice anything so mundane as price, but she did now as she picked out a ladies jacket, in a pinky, creamy beige, the feel of which was like nothing she had ever felt before, it was so soft, not like silk but like cashmere, pliable and begging to be bought. Ann looked at the price ticket. 'Whoa!? How much is that in real money?' All the prices were in Turkish lira.

'Around ninety-five pounds,' Abi said, doing a quick calculation.

Ruth had now reappeared and interrupted them. 'He's going to have to take a closer look at it to give me a quote, so he's going to call me at the hotel later on.'

'Not much chance of you getting it back by tomorrow then?' asked Abi.

'Possibly not, but Toufiq is in Istanbul in a few weeks' time for a conference, he could pick it up for me then.'

So Ruth left the jacket and then left the shop, not realising Ann's love affair with that other jacket. However, the shop didn't call her before they left the hotel the next day. Unfortunately, Toufiq's conference was also cancelled, so Ruth never did get her jacket back. Much as she had wanted it, because Ann had been distracted, she never bought the jacket she'd been drooling over either. She never quite forgave Ruth for that!

The sun was out and they were suitably layered up for the weather so they set off to investigate. While their hotel was actually located in the Fatih district, this particular part of Istanbul was new to them. They hadn't yet explored the area but being part of 'old 'Istanbul' they knew most of the historical sites and buildings in the city were located there. Their main targets for today were the Sultanahmet Mosque (or Blue Mosque) and the museum of Hagia Sophia.

Following the signs they headed past the Topkapi Palace and Museum, which still retained much of the original outer walls.

'I so wanted to go in there,' said Abi. 'There's so much history.'

'If we go in there we won't get to see much else,' said Ann. 'You could spend most of the day wandering around the various courtyards and buildings. I know from when I came with Reza a couple of years ago.'

'Such a shame,' Abi responded.

'Yeah well, we've decided on the Blue Mosque and Hagia Sophia today. Anyway, you'd probably only offer yourself to the harem.'

'Oooh. Now there's a thought!' Abi laughed.

'Time's getting on anyway, we'd never have time to see it all today so let's stick to the plan. Maybe next time?' suggested Ruth.

'Next time? Are you genuinely suggesting we'll ever get to do anything like this again after this week's fiasco?' asked Ann.

'Just can't let it go can you?' Ruth answered.

'Would you?'

'Probably not.' Ruth admitted.

It was a pleasant stroll and in no time at all, they found themselves at Hagia Sophia.

'Wow. Amazing.' Abi gushed. 'Look at that dome, it's fantastic. Just look at the workmanship.'

Ann craned her neck, looking up at the vast crowning glory of the building. 'Apparently, it's a hundred and eight feet in diameter and the pinnacle of it is a hundred and eighty feet above the pavement level. If you think that's impressive wait till you see inside,' Ann gushed.

'I'm a bit confused,' Ruth said. 'Is it a church or a mosque?'

'It was originally built as a cathedral in the sixth century, but then in the fifteenth century it was turned into a mosque when the Ottoman rulers took over,' Ann answered knowledgeably. 'That's when they added the minarets.'

'So why is it called a museum?' Ruth asked.

'It was turned into a museum in 1934 when Hagia Sophia was secularised by the Turkish Government.'

'How do you know all this stuff?' asked Abi.

'I told you. When I came with Reza we did all this. Some I remember and some I checked in my little book,' Ann said, waving it at Abi.

'Bloody know all.'

'Come on, let's get inside.'

'Oh my days, this is beautiful. That dome is even more spectacular from the inside.'

'And look at those lights,' Ruth said, staring at the low-hanging structures suspended from the dome. 'There must be hundreds of bulbs.'

It was thronging with people but the atmosphere inside was hushed, and the height of the dome and ceilings were such that the people below them faded into insignificance. Through the forty windows beneath the dome, the sunlight streaming in seemed unearthly, dappling onto the floor below and casting eerie shadows.

'This is unreal,' said Abi.

They continued walking around, taking in all the Christian iconography on the walls and ceilings, some of which were only partially visible having been painted over during the Ottoman rule.

'Breath-taking,' said Ann, as they came to the mosaic of the Virgin Mary with Jesus as a child, in the apse. She tilted her head back as far as she could, which did her vertigo no good whatsoever, to look up at it. It towered above all the other mosaics they could see, high above them.

'Seems strange to see that Christian mosaic there, and yet here, on these walls and ceilings, there is still evidence of Arabic script,' said Ruth.

'I think it's probably one of the reasons they turned it into a museum, so that arguments about whether it should be a church or a mosque would be forgotten,' ventured Ann.

Abi had been unusually quiet and thoughtful so far, taking in her surroundings in awe, but as she was obsessive about history it wasn't that surprising.

'I guess we'd better go soon,' she said. 'Time is getting on and we still have the Blue Mosque to see. Not sure what time we can go in there till. I don't think it closes as such but they still have prayer services there and the next one will most likely be around sunset.'

'Right. Well we'd better move then,' said Ann as they headed towards the exit door.

Once outside they were pleased that the sun was still relatively high in the sky, meaning they still had time to take in the Blue Mosque and possibly even look at some of the stalls of the street vendors who were selling all sorts of goods.

Walking across the main square outside Hagia Sophia they headed for the Blue Mosque (or Sultanahmet Mosque) which dated back to the seventeenth century. It was originally built to rival the Hagia Sophia, but became popularly known as the Blue Mosque, due to the twenty thousand blue ceramic tiles from Iznik that decorate the walls. (*Iznik is a town in the Bursa region which was once the centre of ceramics in Turkey.*)

Abi decided, that as they would have to remove their shoes to go into the mosque (she had big boots on) and wear head coverings, she would wait outside and take care of Ann and Ruth's belongings while they went inside.

'Are you sure?' asked Ruth.

'Yes. I can't be doing with having to take my boots off and besides, I don't have anything to put on my head. You two have got scarves. It's fine. Go!'

'You've got a scarf on,' Ann pointed at Abi's neck.

'It's not a scarf, it's one of those loopy things,' Abi opened her coat to show Ann.

'Sounds about right for you then,' Ann laughed. 'Being as you're also one of those *loopy things.*'

So, without arguing any further, Ann and Ruth left her waiting outside the door to look after their shoes and coats, and headed for the entrance.

Taking their scarves from around their necks they both covered their heads as custom required. Once inside they again marvelled at the interior. The overriding blueness of the tiles, the light coming in from the two hundred or so stained glass windows, the several chandeliers that hung from the central area, and the richness of the carpets which covered the floor.

'This is something truly special too, isn't it?' Ann said.

'It certainly is,' said Ruth. 'It's a shame we don't have time to look at everything here. We'll only have time for this part.'

After mooching around for some time, enjoying the captivating atmosphere inside the mosque, they decided they had better go back outside and find Abi.

'Never know what she's been up to while we've been in here,' said Ann.

'We haven't been that long,' answered Ruth.

'It doesn't take her long to get up to mischief! She simply can't help herself.'

They hadn't quite reached the steps outside the exit when they heard raised voices, one of which sounded very much like Abi's.

'What the…?' said Ann as she noticed Abi, standing in front of a strange man who was gesticulating wildly at her, which was bad enough, but she then saw Abi's hands were tightly grabbing the lapels of the man's mustard colour jacket.

'Abi? What the hell's going on?'

As Abi had moved further away from the main door and taken their shoes too, Ann and Ruth struggled to reach her, as, without thinking, they raced, barefoot, towards her.

'Will you tell this twonk that I am *NOT INTERESTED* in going to visit his bloody brother-in-law's carpet shop!' Abi almost screamed. 'He's been bugging me for at least twenty minutes and won't take no for an answer.'

In very broken English the man yelled, 'Crazy woman. You will go to hell.'

'You'll be riding around hell on roller skates way before I arrive on my Harley, if you don't get out of my face!' Abi screamed back at him. (Bear in mind that the 'carpet man' was around five foot ten against Abi's five foot two – so she could barely reach his lapels – probably just as well, otherwise it might have been his neck she was squeezing.)

A string of profanities in Turkish then followed, countered by a string of profanities in Arabic from Abi. (It was about the only fluency she had in the language!)

'Abi, come on, let go of him before someone calls the police,' pleaded Ruth.

'Let them,' said Abi. 'He should be locked up.'

'It's not him getting locked up I'm worried about,' said Ann, putting her shoes back on so she could get close enough to Abi to try and unlock her fingers. 'Come on, enough now.'

Finally, Abi loosened her grip and the 'carpet man' quickly disappeared into the small crowd of people who had gathered around them.

'Bloody lunatic. I swear to god if you two hadn't come back then I don't know what I would have done.'

'Can't leave you alone for five minutes can we?' Ann said, looking at Ruth. 'I told you it didn't take long.'

'Well if he hadn't kept on and on about me going to see his carpets...'

'That's what they call it these days is it?' Ann laughed, trying to lighten the mood.

Meanwhile, Ruth was standing quietly by their belongings, which were piled in a heap on the pavement. Very calmly she asked, 'Did he say where

157

his shop is? I would've liked to go and see his carpets.'

'Are you winding me up?' Abi couldn't believe what she had just heard.

At which point Ann couldn't help herself, she suddenly saw the funny side of Ruth's question and hooted with laughter.

'Not funny,' Abi wasn't going to let it go that easily. 'He could have kidnapped me or something.'

'Not much chance of that from what I saw,' Ann mocked. 'You were like a Rottweiler with a bone.'

'So no chance of seeing the carpets then?' Ruth repeated innocently.

'I need a coffee,' Abi scowled at her.

'Let's go over there,' said Ann, pointing to where a number of the street vendors were. 'They've got some nice bits and pieces we could look at later, and meanwhile, we could grab something from one of the stalls selling food and drink. Look, there's a bench over there, by that guy with the samovar.' (a samovar is a big portable tea urn.)

There's surely something uniquely special about sitting in the open air, in the middle of Istanbul, in January, being served tea out of an oversize teapot, from a man in a funny costume, with a friend who is still apoplectic.

'Calmed down yet?' Ann looked at Abi as she sipped her tea, to which she got no response, only a glare.

'You said it's always me that's in trouble,' Ruth said pointedly, looking at Ann.

'There's a first for everything,' Ann replied.

For about half an hour they sat in relative silence, drinking their tea and taking in the sights and sounds around them. There was the impressive sight of the red hues of Hagia Sophia, contrasting with the grandeur of the Blue Mosque with its six minarets, sitting opposite and towering above the square. People of all nationalities milled about, sitting on the walls and benches around the square, cameras clicking in all directions, drinking çay (tea) provided by the street vendors from their samovars, the distant sound of traffic, and the cries of the stallholders trading their wares. And yet, amongst all of this, there remained a sense of tranquillity and calm.

Finally, Abi got up and said, 'You two coming then or what? Or you going to sit there until we freeze to death.'

'Don't exaggerate,' said Ann. 'I should think you're still nicely heated, from the look on your face.'

'I'm fine now. He was such an annoying twonk. Do you know he even offered to take me for lunch after I'd seen his carpets?'

Ruth and Ann looked at each other, trying very hard to suppress their sniggers.

'Good afternoon ladies,' a strange voice said, 'You are English, yes?'

If he says anything about passports I will get physical! Ann thought.

'Yes,' Ruth replied. 'Why do you ask?'

'I have a carpet shop over there…' he started to say as both Ann and Ruth grabbed hold of Abi and promptly marched her away, with Ann calling back over her shoulder 'No thank you. We've had all we can take of carpets for one day.'

Without a backward glance, they hustled Abi towards the few stalls that were around and had a quick meander, looking at what was on offer. Finding nothing any of them wanted to buy they headed towards the main road. They could quite easily have walked back to the hotel, but given the time they flagged down a taxi instead.

Arriving back at the hotel just before six-thirty, Ann suggested they should dump their stuff in the room and then get a cab to the Grand Bazaar to have a quick look around.

'I thought we were doing that tomorrow morning?' asked Ruth.

'I know, but let's go have a quick shufty tonight. We're not going to be doing much else and it is our last night.'

Abi said she didn't mind. She was still a little upset about the earlier incident but didn't take any persuading.

By seven o'clock they were in a cab heading (they thought) towards the Grand Bazaar. Unfortunately, the cab driver spoke neither English nor Arabic but nodded when Ann said where they wanted to go, so they were happy.

After driving around for a while, and appearing to be lost, Ann noticed what she thought was a building she recognised. 'It's around here somewhere,' she said. 'I think I remember that place.

Get him to stop and we'll get out and walk from here.'

'You sure?' asked Abi. 'Looks very quiet and the street lightings not too good.'

'Yes. Come on.'

They managed to signal to the driver to stop and got out of the cab.

'OK, which way?' Abi said.

'I'm sure it's down this way,' Ann replied.

'Not sure I like the look of this,' Ruth sounded unsure.

For around twenty minutes they wandered up and down street after street, none of which remotely resembled the area around the Grand Bazaar, being devoid of shops, stalls, or signs of life. Finally, Ann had to concede she was, in fact, clearly lost.

A smooth, velvety voice seemingly came from out of the darkness of a side street. 'Good evening ladies. Can we help you?'

Turning around they saw two, smart, well-dressed men approaching from across the road.

'We're a bit lost,' Ruth admitted. Walking beside her Ann nudged her hard in the ribs and raised a quizzical eyebrow but said nothing.

'What?' Ruth said, quietly, recognising that for some reason Ann wasn't impressed.

'Too late now!' Ann said. *Talk about the long and the short of it,* she thought. One of the men appeared to be at least six foot six, very slim and swarthy, dressed in a dark overcoat, with a silk cravat at the neck. The other was no more than five foot eight, slicked-back hair, big but not especially overweight, wearing a classic camel-hair coat, unbuttoned, with a suit jacket and waistcoat peeking from underneath. *Look like an older version of Del Boy and Rodney,* Ann laughed to herself, but the hairs on her neck signalling she was, in fact, uneasy at their approach.

'Oh, dear. That's unfortunate,' the shorter of the two said, positioning himself between Ruth and Ann, whilst the other one sidled up to the diminutive Abi.

Ann dropped back a little and walked behind them, not wanting to get involved. The road was otherwise deserted, with little traffic and the street lights only threw small, intermittent, pools of light across the pavement. *Not a very good spot to be approached by two strangers. There's nowhere to go to get away from them. That looks like a main road up ahead but it will take a while before we reach it.* Thoughts whirled through Ann's mind. She couldn't say anything because the two men, by now, were in deep conversation with Ruth and Abi. She couldn't hear exactly what was being said but Abi was not being very chatty, almost to the point of rudeness and Ruth was displaying her usual naïve self by fully engaging with the shorter of the two men, who had attached himself to her.

Being otherwise unengaged, Ann had noticed several people hanging around in doorways and on the corners of a couple of streets they had crossed, which, at the time, didn't worry her too much, but, after walking for around ten minutes, the words "…our hotel is not far…" and "…perhaps you would like to join us for dinner…" reached Ann's ears. *I don't bloody think so!* As another, quite disturbing thought, suddenly flitted through her mind. She decided she needed to do something, and quickly. Speeding up and coming level with Abi she linked arms with her, walking on the outside of the pavement. The main road was almost within sight now.

'Come on,' she said, tugging Abi's arm. 'We need to go.'

'Go where?' Abi hissed.

'Anywhere but here, before Ruth gets us into any more trouble.'

'I don't see there's anything we can do at the moment,' Abi said. 'Why are you so stressed?'

'Did you not hear what "*Del Boy*" said to Ruth?' Ann asked.

'No. I was too busy trying to tell "*Lurch*" (Abi had named him this for some reason) to back off. Why, what did he say?'

'He's trying to get her, and us presumably, to go to their hotel *for dinner*"' Ann replied.

'Oh shit!'

'Exactly! So somehow we need to get her away from him, and quick.'

They both started walking faster, trying to catch up with Ruth and *'Del Boy'* which wasn't too difficult as she was simply slinking along as usual.

With a little manipulation, and coming between her and *'Del Boy'* they managed to get either side of her and linked arms. 'What?' Ruth asked innocently. 'What are you doing?'

Ann, being nearest the pavement, and furthest away from the stranger, whispered, 'Don't even think about accepting his dinner invitation. We need to get away from these two. Like now!'

'I wasn't going to. I'm not completely daft.' Ann and Abi looked at each other sceptically.

The fully lit main road was now only about a hundred yards away, with traffic, including taxis, flowing freely.

'Right, when I say run,' whispered Ann, 'Run.'

Trying to act calm and normal they inched closer to the road.

'RUN,' cried Ann, and the three of them raced away from the two men as fast as their legs would carry them. As luck would have it, a taxi was approaching the junction with the side street as they reached the main road, Abi almost causing an accident by stepping off the pavement into its path.

The taxi screeched to a halt and before the driver knew what was happening the three of them piled in.

'Bisurea.' (Arabic for quickly) Abi shouted, panting and pointing ahead. 'Bisurea.'

'How do you know he speaks Arabic?' Ruth asked.

'I don't, but it was the only word I could think of.'

It seemed that the taxi driver did understand as he took off at speed.

'Thank god we're wearing flats,' said Ann. 'Couldn't have done that in heels.

Tell him to take us to our hotel,' she told Abi.

Abi managed (she hoped) to get the taxi driver to understand where they wanted to go.

'I don't understand. What was the urgency?' Ruth asked.

Abi also looked confused.

'Did you not see those people?' asked Ann.

'What people?' both Abi and Ruth looked puzzled.

'The ones that were hanging about near doorways and on the corners.'

'Oh, those people,' Ruth said. 'Yeah I saw them, what about them?'

'Did I miss something?' asked Abi.

'You didn't notice anything about any of them?'

'Nope.'

'Nope.'

'They were nearly all women!' Ann almost spat the words out.

'And your point is?' asked Abi.

'Oh, my days. Think about it. Dark streets, doorways, women hanging around on corners.'

Abi gasped 'Oh shit!'

'Oh, shit indeed!'

'I still don't get it.' Ruth said.

Ann rolled her eyes and looking at Ruth stated in no uncertain terms 'That stupid twonk of a taxi driver only went and dropped us off in the middle of the Red Light district.'

Ruth looked suitably horrified. 'You're kidding.'

'Wish I'd known earlier; we might have made some extra spending money!' Abi joked.

'You wouldn't?' Ruth asked.

'Why not?' Abi answered, but with a mischievous look in her eyes.

Arriving safely back at their hotel soon after, a little shaken but none the worse for their night-time adventure, they headed straight for the bar.

'I don't know about you two but I definitely need a drink after that,' Ann suggested.

'Your fault. I blame you.' Abi said, glaring at her.

'How come it's my fault?' Ann asked.

'Oooh... Let's go check out the Grand Bazaar before tomorrow. I know where it is. You'll enjoy it!' Abi sarcastically mimicked Ann.

'I thought I did. Besides, you would expect taxi drivers to know where it is. It's only one of the most visited places in Istanbul.'

'Maybe they have another name for it?' Ruth suggested meekly. *(Kapalıçarşı is in fact the Turkish name for it.)*

'Pfft!' (Abi quite liked that expression)

They ordered their drinks and once received sat drinking them, in a subdued mood.

'Maybe we should get an early night,' suggested Ann. 'After all that excitement I don't think I can handle much more tonight. It's our last full day tomorrow and it'll be a very long one.'

'Good idea,' Agreed Abi. 'Let's finish these, go upstairs, and maybe do some packing so we don't have too much to do tomorrow.'

'First sensible thing you've said since we got here,' Ann said.

'How very dare you,' Abi replied.

'Not again you two, please. Let's finish these and go upstairs.'

Once in their room, they each began sorting out their belongings, packing what they no longer needed, and sorting out clothes for the next day. Their flight wasn't until eight the next evening so they pretty much had a full day to do the last-minute sightseeing and the Spice Bazaar and Grand Bazaar would take up most of their time. (If they ever got there.) One by one they finished most of their packing, made a hot drink and all collapsed into bed.

'Do you think that tomorrow, maybe for once this week, we could have a day *without* any dramas?' Ann asked.

'Maybe we could,' said Abi 'But we probably won't.'

Chapter 10
The Bazaars

Ann shivered as she made the tea and coffee the next morning. She wasn't sure of the time, but through the curtains she could just about make out the glow of the street lighting. Opening them, she saw fern-shaped patterns of ice etched onto the glass, and outside snowflakes danced as they swirled down from the sky. *Must be very cold outside,* she thought, but maybe not to herself.

'It's been cold all week,' Abi said drowsily, from the warmth of her bed.

'Yes but today it's extra bloody cold and it's snowing.'

'We'll have to wrap up. I doubt there's any central heating in the bazaar,' Ruth mumbled.

'Did you seriously say that?' Ann looked at her in disbelief.

'But there won't be. Will there?' Ann sometimes had serious doubts about Ruth's logic.

'Can we forget about the heating in the bazaar and get going? I know we have a few hours yet but we have to be back here by four-thirty to be at the airport for six and we still have to finish packing.'

'Slave driver!' Abi responded, dragging herself out of bed.

Already dressed and having finished her tea, Ann said she was heading down to breakfast.

'Why is she always first?' Ruth asked.

'Cos she likes to be in control?'

'No, she doesn't, she's just sooo organised all the time.'

Downstairs in the restaurant, the morning rush for breakfast was underway. As usual, the buffet tables strained under the weight of the food that was laid out. *I'm going to miss this,* Ann thought to herself as she filled her plate, *especially having someone else prepare it all **and** clean up afterward.*

She was beginning to realise that today was their last day of freedom and tomorrow it would be back to the grindstone and responsibilities. She had missed Reza and her boys but...

Abi's voice cut into her thoughts. 'What're you dreaming about?'

'Bloody hell you scared the life out of me,' Ann spluttered, spilling some of her tea as she did so.

'Looked like you were away in fairyland,' said Abi, sitting down opposite.

'I suppose I was. Last day of freedom and all that.'

'Never mind, all good things, etc.'

'Where's Ruth?' asked Ann.

'Faffing as usual. She can't decide what to wear and what to pack. Like a tit in a trance and then she comes out with, "*Ann's always sooo organised.*" She's definitely not. Organised, that is.'

Abi went off to get her breakfast as a serene and relaxed Ruth appeared.

'Where's Abi?'

'Over there,' Ann pointed towards the breakfast table.

'Oh right. I'd better go grab some food too.'

As they were eating, Ann suggested that they have some sort of plan in place for the day.

'What do we need a plan for?' asked Abi.

'To make sure we know where to go to get what we want and don't go meandering off, getting lost,' Ann answered, looking straight at Ruth. 'Do you have any idea how big the Grand Bazaar is? There are over three thousand shops and stalls, sixty-odd streets, and around twenty entrances. Prime conditions to lose each other.'

'We'll never get to see it all today,' Ruth exclaimed.

'My point exactly,' said Ann. 'Which is why we need to know where we're going.'

'Can't we use a map?' asked Ruth, innocently.

'You might as well stick a neon sign on your head flashing *"Tourist"*. I've got maps but there's no way we're using them once we get inside. Let's agree that if any of us does get lost we'll meet up at this gate here, no later than four o'clock,' Ann said, indicating a place on the map she had produced from her 'magic bag'.

'So how are we meant to find that?' Abi asked. 'If we don't have maps.'

'You do,' said Ann passing them one each. 'But try not to get them out inside if you don't want to be hassled. We know where we do want to go and we know where we don't want to go. The streets are organised by product type and the map is colour coded, so it shouldn't be too hard to get around.'

Pointing to a large, green coloured area on the map, Abi said, 'We *definitely* don't want to go there!'

'Why not?'

'Because Ruth, that's where they sell the carpets. There's only so many times I can hear *"Do you want to buy a carpet?"* before I'll be tempted to batter a shopkeeper round the head with something.'

'Been there, done that,' Ann laughed. 'Let's have a stroll down, I don't think it's too far and we can go to the Spice Bazaar first, then on to the Grand Bazaar, and if needs be we can get a cab back later on.'

'Sounds like a plan,' Abi agreed. 'As long as we don't end up where we did last night.' She grinned.

174

Walking outside, the trees and pavements glistened with frost. Ann tied her scarf around her neck, reached into her bag, and produced a navy blue cloche hat, which she promptly popped on her head.

'What the...? Where did that come from?' Abi enquired.

'I bought it the other day in Taksim. Hasn't actually been cold enough so I haven't had a chance to wear it yet but I think I need it today to keep my head warm.'

'Not exactly Royal Ascot, is it?' Abi grinned.

'So. I don't care. It'll keep me warm.'

'Wouldn't catch the Queen wearing it.' Abi smirked.

Ann chose to ignore Abi's remarks and walked away. She couldn't care less who would or would not wear it, it suited her purpose in keeping warm and that's all that mattered. She strode on ahead of her friends, feeling a little bit peeved at Abi's remarks but of course she should have known that wouldn't be the end of it.

They hadn't been walking long when Ann heard, from behind her, a voice calling out in a broad, mocking, East London accent *'Queenie...Queenie.'* *No-one I know*, she thought, and ignored it as she carried on walking. Then, the accent changed to a strong South London accent, as again she heard a voice call out *'Queenie...Queenie.'*

Stopping, turning, and looking around to see who was calling out and to who, she saw Abi and Ruth out of the corner of her eye, holding on to each other and chuckling away to themselves.

'Oh very funny,' she said, even more peeved. 'Stop it you two. Not funny.'

'We think it's hilarious,' said Abi. 'Really suits you. The name, not the hat.'

'Grow up.'

Sticking to the main roads this time, they eventually managed to find their way to the Spice Bazaar. Approaching the entrance, the essence of spice was all-encompassing, wafting through the crisp morning air. Going through one of the two main gates by Tahmis Street, the sight of the original Ottoman stone and Turquoise tiles embellishing the walls and floors, added to the almost magical atmosphere. Aromas of cinnamon, cumin, thyme, saffron, and almost every other type of spice and herb surrounded them, enticing them further in, filling their senses; exotic, expensive, and unique.

While large, due to its 'L' shaped design, the Spice Bazaar was relatively easy to navigate, and similar to the much larger Grand Bazaar, products were arranged according to type.

'If you can't find it here, I doubt you'll find it anywhere,' said Ann, a glazed look showing on her face. 'It feels like it's got its own climate in here, all these scents and colours. Listen to the noise. So many people. With all that body heat who needs central heating?'

'I guess it's okay to take anything back home with us?' asked Ruth.

'Should be alright. They'll pack and label them and as it's not fresh food I think it'll be allowed,' said Abi. 'I know we can get a lot of these from the souk in Dubai, but this is on another level.'

'Just don't go buying any of the 'aphrodisiac' spices,' Ann said, frowning at Ruth. 'We don't want to get arrested again in Dubai.'

Her eyes glinting Ruth answered, 'God you're such a party pooper.'

Meandering up and down the avenues of the 'L' shaped interior, they whiled away an hour or two, steadfastly avoiding the 'tea' being offered by almost every stall they paused at, buying a range of spices for cooking and food, but also some of those recommended for medicinal purposes. Abi's allergies were a concern, so she steadfastly avoided getting too close in case she started sneezing. She had a range of allergies and never knew which one might start her off. Ann bought baklava, Turkish Delight, and Turkish coffee to take back to Reza to earn some brownie points. Ruth acquired some essential oils and essences and Abi bought lots of dried fruits to use in her cooking. They stayed away from the stalls selling textiles, gold and gifts. These were all available in the Grand Bazaar.

Looking at her watch Ann said, 'Right you two, we'd better be making a move soon if we want to do the Grand Bazaar justice. It's getting on for midday now.'

'Blimey! Where did that time go?' Abi said. 'Feels like we've only been in here five minutes.'

Ann scowled, suddenly realising that Ruth was no longer with them. 'Oh for god's sake! Where's she got to now?'

Abi glanced around her, but there was no sign. 'What's she like? Honestly, you have to keep your eyes on her all the time.'

'Did she say there was anything else she wanted in here?' asked Ann.

'No, I thought she was behind me. She can't have gone far. You go that way and I'll head down here. If you find her or reach the end, turn round and we'll meet back here.'

'Ok,' said Ann, walking away in the opposite direction, shaking her head and cursing under her breath. "*Where is she, for god's sake?*" repeatedly checking her watch. "*It's like looking for a needle in a haystack with all these people.. If we don't get a move on we won't have time to see anything.*" Hurrying now, she glanced this way and that, looking into shops as she went but without seeing any sign of Ruth.

Fifteen minutes later she gave up and started walking back to where she had left Abi, hoping she had had more success, but it appeared that Abi too was now missing and Ann could feel the tension in her neck and shoulders increasing with every second, as she paced up and down outside the shop.

'Found her,' Abi called as she reappeared from the crowd. 'Faffing about buying spices that she doesn't need!'

'Sorry, I didn't realise you two had moved on,' said Ruth, fidgeting with her bags and glancing sideways at Ann. 'Then when I turned around you'd gone.'

'Whatever,' said Ann, through narrowed eyes. 'Can we get a move on now. It's around twenty-five minutes walk to the Grand Bazaar from here and we're running out of time.'

'Let's grab a taxi,' suggested Abi. 'It'll be quicker and easier and give us time to have a quick coffee when we get there.'

'Coffee?' Ann asked, incredulous, but agreed to the taxi, which subsequently dropped them off at the Carsikapi entrance of the bazaar.

They wandered inside into an overwhelming cornucopia of people, colours, and aromas. Into a labyrinth of narrow, ancient alleyways, covered by high domed arches; lamps of different shapes, sizes, and colours, hanging from the ceilings of the stalls, glowing like a constellation. It was other-worldly, a place where history seemed to have morphed into the present, where local culture intertwined with tourism, and the babble of a thousand languages filled the air.

Abi's eyes were like saucers as she looked around. A wide smile graced Ann's face and Ruth, like a giddy child took a few steps forward, turned around, and skipped back, her eyes alight with pleasure.

'Right, there's a couple of coffee shops over there,' said Ann, pointing to her left. 'Quick cuppa and we'll have a look at where we want to go and what we want to see. You two are looking for specific things aren't you?'

'Yes, there's a couple of bits I want to get for the kids, nothing much though.'

'Me too,' said Ruth.

'Okay. I suggest you find where we are on that map and work out where you're most likely to find them. There's nothing I particularly want, although I might get a tulip tea set if I can find one, so I'll meander around and meet you two back here later. It's easy to get lost so *stay together*,' said Ann.

'You not coming with us then?' Abi asked.

'No. I'm sure I'll be fine on my own and I'll only get agitated if I keep getting dragged off to look at things I'm not interested in. I think you two need the stalls and streets on the left, over here, and I'm going to head down there to the right to look at the leather goods and then make my way to the central bit and antiquey type stuff. If I have time, I'll finish up in the souvenir bit at the end.'

'We can always look at our maps,' said Ruth.

Ann raised her eyebrows. 'Don't forget what I said about neon lights and maps. Use it as little as possible.'

'Oh, right. Ok then.'

Abi had ordered the coffee, and tea for Ann, and was now frantically rummaging around in her bag.

'Oh crap!' she said.

'What? Oh crap, what?' Ann held her breath.

'My purse. I can't find my purse!'

'What?' Ruth gasped. 'You must have it. You had it earlier. You bought all that dried fruit.'

'State the bloody obvious why don't you,' Abi cried aloud.

'Calm down,' Ann said evenly. 'Sit down, slow down and look carefully. Have you put it in one of the side pockets?'

'No.'

'When did you last have it?' Ann asked.

'When I put it in my bloody bag.'

'OK, no need to be narky.'

Ruth sat quietly, watching and listening.

Abi emptied her bag of all its contents, her hands shaking, as she checked all the zipped compartments and main sections, in vain.

'What the hell am I going to do now?' she asked, her voice quivering as she spoke. 'All my cards, money, and travellers' cheques are in it.'

Ann's was the voice of reason. 'Don't let's panic just yet. Check the bags with your shopping in, maybe you dropped it in one of those.'

Ruth picked the bags up from the floor, and crossing her fingers under the table as she did so, handed them over to Abi who carefully removed her shopping from each of the bags. Abi soon realised her purse was in none of those either.

'So how did you pay for the coffees?' Ann asked.

'I didn't. That's why I came back to get my purse.'

'Oh right. So the last time you remember having it was at the spice bazaar?'

'Yes. I bought the fruit and nothing after that. I'm sure I put it in my bag then.'

'Maybe you dropped it somewhere? You don't think someone stole it do you?' Ruth said.

'Obviously, it's got to be one of those two,' snapped Abi. 'Oh for god's sake, is there any point in going back there? If I did drop it, it'll be long gone by now.'

'No, I don't see the point,' Ann agreed. 'If you dropped it there you're not going to find it now. Unless you dropped it in the cab on the way here? We could try ringing the taxi firm but I sure as hell wouldn't know how to start finding their number. Did they give you a receipt when you paid Ruth?'

'Err. I don't think so.'

'Could you have a look then? You paid for it. Can't you remember?' Ann asked.

'No, I can't, but I don't remember getting a receipt,' Ruth started to delve into her bag for her purse.

'Please don't tell me you've lost yours too,' Ann said through gritted teeth.

'Don't be silly,' Ruth answered. 'Of course I haven't. It's here,' she said pulling a long, slim, zipped, red purse from her bag.

'What the…' Abi spluttered 'That's not your bloody purse. It's mine.'

Ruth looked more closely at the offending purse in horror. 'How did that get in my bag?'

'You've got to be kidding me! First, you don't know what your own passport looks like and now you don't know what your own purse looks like. Which is where, by the way?' Ann glared at her.

Reaching back into her bag Ruth produced a completely different purse. Different in size, shape, and colour. 'Here it is,' she said shakily, holding up a stubby brown purse with a clasp.

'That still doesn't explain how my purse got in your bag. We've wasted time, got panicked and stressed out and all the time it was languishing in your bag?' Abi was obviously unimpressed.

Ruth gave a nervous smile. 'I remember now. When you paid for the fruit you passed it to me to hang on to till you put your stuff away in the shopping bag. I must have put it in my bag, but then Ann came along and said we needed to go, and I sort of forgot.'

'Sort of forgot? Honestly! Didn't you see it when you paid for the taxi?' Abi growled at her.

'Look you've got it now so can we get a move on before we run out of time completely,' Ann said, sweeping up her bags from the floor and pushing her chair back roughly.

'I'm sorry,' Ruth said, through lowered lids.

'You will be,' Abi snapped back.

Ann could feel the first signs of a headache starting. She stood there, eyes closed, and took a deep breath before saying 'I'm going this way,' pointing to her right. 'If we don't catch up before, then I'll see you both, where we agreed, at four o'clock.' With that, she strode away.

Ruth swallowed hard, her cheeks awash with a rosy flush, her eyes following Ann's disappearing figure. 'Do you think she's annoyed with me?' she asked, glancing at Abi.

'Nah! She'll get over it. Come on,' Abi said, striding away in the opposite direction, Ruth trotting along behind her.

Ann, meanwhile, sensed a knot in her stomach. *I was a bit harsh there. It was a genuine mistake but…* She began to regret her shortness with Ruth. *I'll have to find a way to make it up to her later.* Following the map in her mind's eye, she headed towards the area where she knew she would find the leather goods. She didn't actually need the map, she could have simply followed her nose, the distinctive aroma of leather alone would have led her there.

Oh my. Wow. Look at all these goodies. She wandered along, much calmer now and her headache started to recede, despite the constant noise of the vendors shouting their wares and the general cacophony of sounds all around her.

Coming across a stall selling handbags and purses, which she thought was a little ironic, she couldn't resist taking a closer look. Hidden amongst all the belts, bags, and purses she saw a glimpse of something bright yellow and like a magpie was instantly attracted to it. It was, in fact, a medium-size box with a clear lid. Picking it up and seeing the contents, she couldn't help but smile. *Perfect!* she giggled to herself. She also bought a leather wallet for Reza, a soft leather belt for her eldest son, and a snazzy, soft leather jerkin for her youngest.

Pleased with the purchases she headed towards the central square to immerse herself in the antique items on show. There was so much to choose from but she couldn't resist a brown-coloured, Turkish/Morrocan-style temple lamp for candles. *That would look fabulous in the lounge on a winter's night.* She did wonder whether it would fit in her case but when she lifted it, it wasn't at all heavy. In keeping with custom, she bartered with the stallholder on the price and couldn't believe it when she was able to purchase it for less than half what he originally wanted.

I only need the tulip tea set now, if I can find one, and I suppose I'd better get something for cow bag as well to say sorry. She left the central square and headed for the souvenir area. Mindful of the crowds she kept a tight hold of her belongings, her handbag and especially her purse. *Hope those two are keeping an eye on their stuff too.*

In the meantime, Ruth and Abi were strolling along Fesciler Street, wending their way in and out of the sheer number of people around, taking in all the stalls where you could buy anything from a Fez to a t-shirt or jeans. There was so much choice they struggled to decide what to buy and both ended up with much more than they had intended. T-shirts, sweatshirts, jeans, and more. With six children between them, it added up to quite a sizeable addition to their luggage.

'Do you think she's calmed down yet?' Ruth asked, struggling to make herself heard above the din.

'Yeah. You know what she's like, quick to anger, quick to cool. She'll be fine and is probably feeling very bad and a little bit silly right now,' Abi answered loudly.

'So, what now? There's nothing else here I'm particularly interested in looking at,' Ruth said.

'I think if we keep walking straight down here it'll take us to the souvenir section. We'll probably find Ann there too,' Abi sounded confident.

'Hmmm. You sure she'll be OK now?'

'Stop being a wuss! What's the worst that could happen? She's probably been hypnotised by the smell of leather and the sparkle of all the shiny things in the antique area.'

Ruth was less than convinced but, nevertheless, followed Abi who sauntered along, constantly checking right and left to make sure she wasn't missing any bargains to be had, keeping her bag very close to her body.

Eventually, they reached the area where souvenirs of all descriptions could be found. From the bright blue and white evil-eye amulets (Nazar Boncuğu) to ward off evil spirits, samovars, and small prayer rugs, to mint and apple tea. Turkish delight in rose red and mint green, pistachio nougat, and dark rich Turkish coffee. Copper spice sets and the brilliant blue hues of Turkish ceramics. Everything was there to be had.

Ann was completely engrossed in her surroundings; so much to see and buy. She wasn't an impulsive shopper by nature but… how could anyone resist? She spotted the tulip tea set she wanted and also ended up with three different types of Turkish delight, a copper spice set, a few variations on the Nazar Boncuğu for friends and colleagues as well as several packets of mint and apple tea. She also found a beautiful blue silk scarf for Abi, which she hoped would put her back in the good books. It was as well she had left plenty of room in her suitcase and that there hadn't been a partridge in a pear tree for sale anywhere.

She had so far resisted the relentless efforts of the stallholders to tempt her inside for tea, which was freely offered at practically every stall she stopped to look at, but she began to feel the need to roll her neck from side to side and rotate her shoulders to loosen them a little. Feeling suddenly weary she felt she could do with a hot drink and a sit-down.

Above the noise of the crowds, she unexpectedly heard a familiar voice, not calling her exactly but she knew who it was all the same. *Queenie…Queenie.* She felt a smile spread across her face. *Silly mare* she thought, turning in the direction of the voice. *Queenie…Queenie.*

Pushing their way towards her she could make out Ruth and Abi, both laden with bags and parcels.

In an attempt to put their little skirmish to one side she gestured animatedly. 'Come on you two, I've found the perfect gift for you to take back to Mitri, Abi!' she said as she, for once, went inside one of the shops. Abi and Ruth followed, not seeing any evidence outside of what this *perfect gift* might be. Inside Ann had taken a chair and was being given the much-needed tea she so desperately sought.

'What? Where?' asked Abi, still unable to see what this particular shop could possibly offer.

Ruth, however, spotted exactly what Ann meant and smiled to herself. *She's not going to be amused.*

'Can't you see? Take a look around you,' Ann grinned widely.

'What…? You dozy mare,' Abi suddenly realised what *gift* Ann was talking about. 'No way. Don't be ridiculous!'

'Go on. He'd love it.'

'Yes. Go on. Go and try one on,' Ruth joined in, as she also took a chair and the proffered cup of tea.

'There is no way I am going to try any of those on,' Abi was adamant.

'Where's the harm? You'll get a cup of coffee in exchange,' Ann's eyes twinkled at the thought.

'No...No...No!'

The vendor meanwhile was sizing Abi up, and spreading before her all colour and manner of belly-dancing costumes, complete with veil, skirt, bra, hip scarf be-decked with coins, even down to the finger cymbals.

Ruth was beginning to enjoy herself. 'You're always showing off your belly dancing skills at parties and stuff. With one of these, you could definitely go to town.'

'I. AM. NOT. GOING. TO. TRY. ONE. OF. THESE. ON.'

'You could at least try to appear as though you're interested and have a look so we can finish our tea,' Ann took another sip of hers, lowering her head but keeping her eyes firmly on Abi.

'Yes, go on,' Ruth was getting into the spirit.

'You two are beyond belief. Ok. Ok. I'll look, but that's it!' Abi finally succumbed to the pressure.

'Get one for yourself and one for Natalie (Abi's daughter) then you can teach her how to dance too.' Ann was so into the banter now.

'They're quite nice actually, good quality but I'm still not buying one.'

They eventually left the shop, with Abi having two extra parcels to add to her collection.

'I can't believe you made me buy these.'

'But think of Mitri's face when he sees it,' Ann smiled.

'He'll probably divorce me on the spot.'

'Nah! He'll love it, you wait and see.'

Ruth was staying quiet.

Time was marching on now and the three were conscious that they needed to get back to the hotel, so they headed towards the exit where they had originally arrived earlier on.

'Did you get everything you wanted?' Ann asked.

'Yes, and some things I didn't want,' Abi said, pointedly.

Ruth looked worried. 'I've got no idea how I'm going to get all this into my case.'

'You'll manage. If push comes to shove we can put some in my case. I should have a fair bit of space,' Ann was trying to be conciliatory but any bad feeling had already disappeared and the three friends were back to their normal selves.

They managed to flag a taxi down without too much difficulty and, along with all their purchases, were soon back at their hotel.

Miray was in reception and her eyes widened as she saw the three women entering the foyer, weighed down with all their bags and parcels. 'It looks as though you have had an enjoyable day ladies.'

'Very nice,' said Ruth. 'We got a bit carried away and we bought much more than we intended to.'

'This is always the way when you go to the Bazaar. So many things to see and buy. You are happy with your purchases?'

'Very,' said Ann, although Abi gave her a sideways look.

'If we take these upstairs now can we get something to eat before we leave?' Ruth, for once the sensible one, realised they hadn't eaten much all day and would probably not get anything until much later that night.

'Of course madam. The restaurant is open. What would you like?'

'A hot meze would probably be best if that's possible?'

'I will see to it. Shall we say, in fifteen minutes?'

'That would be perfect,' Ann thanked her.

'Right, let's get this lot upstairs come back down and eat and then finish packing?' Ann suggested.

'How long have we got?' asked Ruth.

'It's a little after four,' Ann said looking at her watch. 'If we can finish eating by around five, be packed by five-thirty, get a cab for five-forty-five, then we should make it to the airport for around six.'

'We won't have time to shower or anything then?' Abi said.

'Unfortunately not, unless you want to go without eating or we get finished packing earlier. We have to be at the airport as close to six as we can.'

'Ok. No worries.'

Once upstairs, they dumped all their stuff on the floor and the beds, where their cases sat open, and went straight back down to the restaurant.

Miray caught sight of them coming out of the lift and pointed towards a table she had set out for them, gesturing to the waiter as she did so, to bring the food.

All three collapsed on a chair, exhausted from all the walking, the shopping, and just occasionally, being stroppy with each other. They were looking forward to relaxing for this short while to replenish their stomachs and their minds.

As always the food was tasteful and plentiful.

'That hit the spot,' Ann felt so much better now.

'Definitely. I hadn't realised how hungry I was,' Ruth enthused.

'Too much for me,' Abi, as usual, hadn't eaten a great deal.

'Right then, let's get to it. I'll go and ask Miray to order us a taxi for the airport. I'll see you two upstairs,' Ann pushed her chair back and stood up.

Ruth looked at Abi. 'I'm so glad we're Ok now. I hate it when we fall out.'

'But we don't really, do we? We spat, yes spat, that's a good word, but we never seriously fall out. Come on, we'd better get a move on. Can't afford to be late getting to the airport.'

Their hotel room looked like a shopper's paradise, with bags and goods strewn on the beds, chairs, and floor.

'Are we going to get all of this into our cases?' Ruth wasn't convinced.

'Okay, let's put it this way. If you don't, you'll have to leave it behind. Apart, maybe, from my lamp, nothing is too big or too heavy, so I'm sure we can squeeze it all in,' Ann, as usual, was sublimely confident.

Practically in silence, they each set about working out the best way to fit everything in. Luckily they all had expanding cases, so it was easier than they thought it might be.

Ann, of course, finished first, with Abi running a close second. Ruth's case was bulging at the seams but they managed to get it closed. Then Abi noticed a couple of packages on Ann's bed.

'Oi! Miss Organised. You've left some stuff out,' she said.

'No I haven't…actually, yes I have, but on purpose. I wanted to say sorry for earlier so I bought you both a little gift,' she said as she handed them over.

'Awwwh! Ya big softie!' Abi was almost emotional for once. Opening her package she smiled. 'You know me so well,' she said, admiring the scarf Ann had bought her.

'Ooooh. What's this?' Ruth took the box out of the bag. Once she realised she let out a shriek of laughter.

'What is it?' Abi asked.

'It's perfect,' Ruth said, as she opened the box and withdrew a bright yellow purse, together with a matching passport holder.

'They're pretty hard to miss,' Abi also laughed. 'Should both be easy to find now, eh!'

'Glad you like them,' Ann smiled at her friends. Perfick!

Looking at her watch Abi announced it was almost five-thirty. They did a quick last check of the room and bathroom and, satisfied they had packed everything, took their cases outside and locked the door.

Once in reception, they left them by the desk and for the last time sat in the foyer to wait for their taxi. They had said their goodbyes to the staff and were all, it must be said, feeling a little emotional. It had been one hell of a week.

Ruth was looking for something in her bag when she let out a squeal.

'Oh no.'

'What now?' Ann asked, not wanting to know the answer.

'My passport. I can't find my passport!'

Abi leapt from her chair. 'Don't be bloody ridiculous. You can't have lost it again.'

Ruth raised her head, her eyes merry with glee. 'Gotchya!' she cried, looking from Abi to Ann. 'Oh, I wish you could see your faces.'

If either of them had had anything to hand there is no doubt they would have launched it at Ruth's head.

'Silly mare!' but Ann was grinning as she said it.

Miray called to them. 'Ladies... Your taxi is outside.'

They collected their cases and went outside to the taxi, followed by Miray and several of the hotel staff. 'Goodbye ladies, have a safe journey. We have enjoyed having you stay with us and hope you will come back again soon.'

That pushed Ruth over the edge, as she waved to them all with tears in her eyes. Ann was also welling up but Abi, as always, kept her emotions in check.

As the taxi pulled away Ann said 'I doubt we will ever forget these five days in Istanbul.' Ruth and Abi nodded in agreement.

Chapter 11
The Return

Despite it being Friday night and rush hour, the taxi made good time to the airport, arriving shortly after six o'clock.

Ann went off to find a trolley for their luggage while Ruth and Abi waited by the taxi rank.

'I'm sort of not looking forward to going home,' Ruth said. 'I am but I'm not sure how Toufiq will be about everything.'

'He'll have got over it by now,' Abi tried to reassure her. 'He'll just be pleased to see you back safe and sound and not incarcerated in some Turkish prison.'

'You think?'

'Definitely. What's done is done and Toufiq isn't one to hold on to negative stuff is he?'

'Guess not.'

Ann arrived with the trolley, and with a lot of huffing and puffing, they loaded everything onto it and headed inside to find their check-in desk.

They were all a bit concerned as they handed over their passports but thankfully they were handed back, together with their boarding passes and they watched their cases disappear behind the conveyor belt curtain.

Ann hadn't realised she'd been holding her breath. 'Phew,' she said. 'Hurdle number one out of the way.'

'What do you mean hurdle number one? How many more do you think there will be?' Ruth sounded concerned.

'None I hope but knowing our luck...'

'Don't wind her up,' Abi stuck up for her friend.

'I'm not, but until we land safely at Dubai airport I'm not taking anything for granted.'

'Do you honestly think there will be any more trouble?' Ruth asked.

'Nah! It'll probably be fine,' said Ann, crossing her fingers behind her back.

With their luggage, hopefully, on its way to the plane, they headed towards the departure gates to find somewhere to sit where they could see the flight information boards. None of them wanted to take a chance on missing the gate call, they only had about ninety minutes before they should be boarding.

'Let's grab a coffee and sit here and relax for a while,' Ann suggested. 'I don't know about you two but I'm pooped after today. Glad we ate at the hotel, at least now we can hopefully get some sleep on the plane.' Abi doubted that was going to happen for her.

While Abi and Ruth went off to get the drinks, Ann stayed to keep one eye on their belongings and the other on the departure boards for updates. *Let's hope we don't have any more issues.* Nagging doubts still plagued her mind.

Abi and Ruth returned with the drinks, some pastries, and some treats for the plane, and they all sat in quiet contemplation. They were so close to being safely home and yet in some ways so far.

Thirty minutes passed in the blink of an eye and Ann, for some reason was becoming fidgety. She didn't know why but… 'Come on you two, let's head over to passport control. We only have around an hour so we should be boarding before too long. We can as easily sit in the departure lounge as here.' She was feeling the need to get through the next hurdle.

There was no argument from either Abi or Ruth, so they collected up their coats and bags and headed towards the departure and immigration area.

The queues weren't too bad at all and it didn't take them long to move forward. Ann suddenly froze as they reached the end of the line.

'No way. I don't bloody believe it,' she muttered, her eyes firmly on the window of the passport booth.

'What? What's wrong?' Abi was feeling panicked. 'Don't tell me you can't find something now.'

Ruth, meantime, as a default, had gone pale as she looked up and saw what Ann had seen. 'No. It can't be. It just can't be.'

'What the hell is wrong with you two?' Abi was also now a little concerned.

'Look,' said Ann, trying to subtly point at the booth.

Abi finally saw the cause of her friends' consternation. 'Oh for Christ's sake. You couldn't make it up could you?'

Sitting at the desk in the booth was the same officer who had been on duty the day they'd arrived.

'I can't do it,' Ruth was shaking with nerves. 'I can't face him again. Here, one of you two will have to give him my passport.'

'What's he gonna do?' Abi couldn't be doing with histrionics. 'Anyway, do you honestly think he's going to remember you from the thousands of people he must have seen this week?'

Ruth, trying to become inconspicuous, shuffled behind Ann and Abi, as Ann handed over the passports for inspection.

The officer took them from her, opening them up at the information page before stamping them with the appropriate exit visas. All seemed fine until it wasn't. Hesitating, he looked down at the passport in his hand, looked up searching their faces to compare them with the photographs, paused again, and with what could be mistaken for a smile, said in very broken English, 'Aaah! You English lady, no passport.' Ruth almost collapsed on the spot and Abi had to grab hold of her arm to stop her from dropping to the floor. 'No baby now? It's good now, yes?' With that, he stamped all three passports and handed them back, adding 'You had good time. Yes?' His smile was more visible now.

'Thank you, yes, we did,' Ann finally managed to say, as she and Abi hauled Ruth away before she crumpled into a heap.

Getting her to a seat they plonked her down, one sitting either side of her for support.

'I don't think I ever want to travel again,' Ruth almost sobbed with relief.

'Don't be such a drama queen,' Abi was laughing now at the absurdity of it. 'It's all fine.'

'Hurdle number two out of the way,' Ann muttered under her breath, which luckily Ruth didn't hear.

'*Flight TK1959 now boarding at gate number 7*' came over the tannoy.

'That's us,' said Ann, relieved to hear the announcement. 'Now pull yourself together and let's get on that plane.'

Ruth didn't need telling twice, as, still visibly shaken, she picked up her bag and almost stumbled along beside her friends.

Soon they were aboard the plane and once the usual debate about the window seat was settled (Ann won this time) they sat down, breathed a sigh of relief, and looked forward to the journey.

Chapter 12
The Homecoming

Eventually, the lights dimmed and the cabin noise became hushed. All of them, including Abi, slept throughout the flight. It was only the noise of the landing gear and flaps being deployed, that stirred them from their slumbers.

Ann stretched, still groggy and bleary-eyed. Through the window, she could see the blackness of the desert below with the lights of Dubai in the distance. 'Oh cripes! We'd better stir our stumps, we'll be landing in a few minutes.'

'Do we have to?' Ruth yawned.

'What? Get moving or land? A safe landing is preferable to anything else, don't you agree?' Ann quipped.

'I need coffee.' Abi said from behind still closed lids.

'We will shortly be landing in Dubai.' A phantom voice announced over the intercom. *'Please fasten seat belts, put tables into the upright position, and place all your bags on the floor in front of you.'*

There was an echo of clicks throughout the cabin as most people complied. The cabin crew quickly reacted to anyone trying to remove luggage from the overhead lockers.

'Plonkers!' was Ann's verdict. She was quite happy to sit and relax until they were down and back on terra firma, as the landing was her least favourite part of any flight. She exhaled loudly as the wheels touched down and the plane slowed to a crawl.

There was the usual melee of people rushing to retrieve their luggage before the aircraft had come to a stop, jostling for position and hoisting bags from the overhead lockers, with little regard for other passengers.

'Christ! Good job we're all relatively short,' Abi observed. 'That idiot only just missed my head.'

'Might have knocked some sense into you,' Ann folded her arms and relaxed back into her seat, as the terminal came into view through her window.

'I'm in no rush,' Ruth mumbled to herself.

'Can't say I'm surprised. You wouldn't be, would you? Look don't worry, everything will be fine. What's the worst that could happen?' Ann wasn't sure who she was trying to convince.

When the initial dash was over Abi stood and stretched up to try and open the overhead locker. 'Get out of the way shorty. Let me do it or we'll be here all night,' Ruth said, as she began to haul everything down.

'Charming!'

'No, honestly, you're really so horizontally challenged you'd never reach.'

Ann meantime was still sitting, quite relaxed, waiting for her turn to start unloading.

Finally, they had all retrieved their bags and belongings and made their way off the plane. They joined the line of people heading towards the buses waiting to transport them to the terminal building and passport control.

Joining the queue for British and European passport holders, Ann suddenly had a thought. One which she wished she hadn't had. Deciding to keep it to herself, just in case she was being paranoid, she kept slowly moving forward, making sure that the three of them kept together, but the closer they got to the booth, the more she had a sense of foreboding. *Let's hope I'm wrong about hurdle number three.*

They moved forward together to the window. Sweating slightly and with clammy palms, Ann handed over their passports. The officer behind the glass checked them individually, checking for their resident visa status. He then began flicking through the various pages.

'Where have you come from?' he spoke directly to Ann, who tried hard to meet his eyes. 'Istanbul,' she almost whispered her reply. He seemed happy with two of the passports, but with the third, he kept on flicking. *Oh shit!* Ann couldn't bear the suspense.

Holding the passport up, his eyes travelled across the faces before him. He then gestured for Ruth to come forward. *Here we go.* Ann's nightmare thought began to unfold.

'Madam, I see you have an entry visa into Turkey,' he focused on Ruth's face. 'Where is your exit visa from Dubai?'

Abi, who had evidently not had the same thought as Ann, gasped, looking frantically at Ruth, who in turn looked as if she might crumble into a heap any second.

Don't try to blag it! Ann thought, as she reached out to steady Ruth.

'Exit visa?' the immigration officer repeated.

Abi stepped forward. 'There was a bit of a mix-up with my friend's passport,' she smiled sweetly, hoping she could keep her nerve 'which we didn't realise until we arrived in Istanbul.'

'Ye…ye…yes,' Ruth muttered. 'I picked up the wrong passport when I left home but nobody realised until we arrived at Istanbul airport.'

'This is not possible!' The immigration officer seemed less than convinced.

'It shouldn't be but that's what happened,' Abi tried to convince him.

For the second time in five days, the queue behind them was becoming agitated at the delay.

'Please madam, step to one side while I deal with the remaining passengers,' With that, he called another officer over, speaking to him in Arabic and handing him their passports. This second officer motioned, in no uncertain terms, for them all to follow him. *Here we go again, thought Ann, not believing what was happening.*

This time all three found themselves seated in the security office, minus their passports.

'Listen, it'll be alright,' Ann tried to console Ruth, who was visibly shaking. 'Where's Jay's passport and the paperwork they gave you in Istanbul?'

'I have Jay's passport here,' said Ruth taking it out of her bag. 'They didn't give me anything else though, not once they stamped my passport in Istanbul, and they took the temporary visa too. What's going to happen now?'

'I think we're about to find out,' Ann nodded towards the door where two new officers had entered, heading in their direction. Ruth and Abi followed her gaze.

The three security officers herded them, separately, through a door and along a windowless, soulless corridor before they were shown into individual rooms.

Ann took a seat, her palms increasing in sweatiness and her breath coming in short, shallow, bursts. *Oh my god, if this is how I'm feeling what the hell is Ruth going through?*

In her room, Abi kept smiling sweetly in the hopes it would win her brownie points for being a nice, blameless person.

Ruth was trembling from head to foot as she, unsteadily, lowered herself into the chair that she was guided to. Feeling faint she asked for a glass of water and reached into her bag for some tissues to wipe away the sweat that began to appear on her top lip.

All three were kept there and questioned steadily for nearly two hours, about their Istanbul trip and the issues with Ruth's exit stamp. How she had managed to leave Dubai with only her son's passport, and why she hadn't realised her mistake. Why no one in passport control had noticed? Of course, none of them had the answers.

The phone in Ann's room started to ring and the officer got up to answer it. Replacing it, he then opened the door and left. Ann was suddenly distracted by noises outside in the corridor, and as the door to her room opened again, she was sure she was about to be arrested, so when the senior officer, who had entered, spoke, she almost fell off her chair. 'Madam, you are free to rejoin your friends.'

Not wishing to appear too eager to get away Ann thanked him, her voice trembling. She stood up, collected her bags, and walked as slowly as she could from the room.

Outside Abi and Ruth were waiting for her. Ruth's face was pallid but Abi was grinning like a Cheshire cat.

The original officer, who had escorted them from the passport control area, took them to the luggage collection carousels, where their luggage was still on the conveyor belt, going round and round like the horses you see on fairground roundabouts. No-one spoke.

Loading their cases onto a trolley, the security officer escorted them from the area and pointed towards the exit sign.

Once the doors closed behind them, leaving them alone in the corridor, Ruth finally let go, howling into Ann's shoulder. 'Oh my god! I was sure they were going to lock me up.'

'I don't know what happened there,' Ann said, 'I thought we'd had it, they kept on asking me the same questions over and over, then the phone rang and next thing I know they're telling me I can leave.'

'Same here,' Ruth was still sobbing.

'Well… say "Thank you" to me,' Abi chimed in.

'What? Why the hell have we got to say thank you to you?' Ann looked quizzical.

'I was the same as you, they kept asking me the same questions over and over. I was getting majorly fed up with it and wondering what the heck Mitri would be thinking and what sort of mood he'd be in as he's coming to pick us up. He won't be impressed at having had to hang around for two hours. Then it hit me.'

'What? What? Don't keep us in suspense. I don't see what Mitri picking you up has got to do with us being allowed to go?' Ann's voice was getting high-pitched.

'Do you remember Hussain Al Jeera? You met him a couple of times at our place.'

'Yes, I remember him, and ...?' Ann still failed to see the relevance.

'So, when I was thinking about Mitri, Hussain popped into my head for some reason.'

'Get on with it woman.'

'He works here, at the airport. Something to do with airport security, quite high up in the pecking order.' Abi couldn't contain her pleasure at this little gem.

'What?' Ruth finally found her voice.

'What? You mean to say you know someone who is in the hierarchy of this airport and it took you two bloody hours to remember it?' Ann almost spat the words.

'No. It was only about an hour ago when I started worrying about what Mitri, and probably Reza, would be thinking that Hussain came to mind. It took me a while to get them to listen to me but as soon as I mentioned his name, and said that he was a friend of my husband, things changed.'

'What changed?' Ruth sounded sceptical.

'More or less everything basically. The two security people looked at each other, stopped asking me questions and suddenly left the room. They didn't say a thing, just walked out.'

'So… God, it's like trying to get blood out of a stone woman. Spit it out,' Ann's voice was going up another notch.

'They left me sitting there for about half an hour and the next thing Hussain walked into the room, full of apologies to me and swearing at the two security guys in Arabic.'

'How do you know he was swearing?' Ruth seemed to think, amongst all of the possible questions she could ask, this was the most important.

'Seriously? Is that all you're worried about?' Ann couldn't help herself. 'OK Abi, so he was swearing, then what?'

'He had all our passports, including Jay's, in his hand. He gave them all back to me, left the room, and said he would be waiting for us outside to take us along to the immigration office and sort this out. He's also sent someone to find Mitri and Reza to let them know what's happening.'

Hussain was indeed waiting for them, full of apologies for their detainment and assuring them that, once they had been to the immigration office, they would be free to go.

They followed him along the corridor to the main office where the staff on duty all stood up when he entered. He had a natural air of authority and spoke, in an imposing voice, in Arabic, gesturing all the while with his hands. Within a very short space of time, Ruth was in possession of further paperwork and Hussain explained what she would need to do.

'So madam Ruth, the problem is, that according to your passports and exit and entry visas, your son left the country but hasn't returned. On the other hand, you have never left the country but have come back. This is a problem for our records, your son's school, your employment, and indeed your passports.'

Ruth's mouth dropped open. 'I didn't think of all that.'

'You're going to have to bloody well think about it now,' said Ann, who hated anything disorganised and it seemed that Ruth's whole life at the moment was exactly that.

Paperwork and passports in hand, belongings, and luggage trollied, they headed towards

213

the exit doors. It was now two-forty-five in the morning.

'I'm so glad Toufiq isn't picking me up,' Ruth uttered, slowly shaking her head, her eyes closed. 'I don't think I could stand any more questions tonight.'

'Yeah, let's hope Reza and Mitri are feeling understanding,' Ann dragged her hands through her hair, a slight sheen of sweat appearing on her forehead.

'Mitri won't say anything. Not while you're in the car Ruth but I'll probably get both barrels when we get home, or he might say nothing, which is probably worse.' Abi wasn't sure which she preferred.

As they approached the final door before the arrivals hall, all three took a deep breath.

'Smiles on girls. Smiles on!' Ann hesitated before giving the door a push.

They saw Mitri and Reza, talking animatedly with Hussain who had quickly found his way to them via internal walkways. All three turned as the women appeared.

'Hi, darling,' Ann waved at Reza, trying to appear calm and collected. He smiled back but his face showed his concern.

'Bloody hell! Are you OK?' he asked.

'Yes, fine,' Ann was encouraged by his smile.

'You two OK?' He looked at Abi and Ruth.

'I will be once we get home,' Ruth said shakily.

214

'You know me,' Abi grinned, not wanting to look too closely at Mitri.

But she needn't have worried. He too was full of concern.

Outside, they separated. Ruth and Abi followed Mitri to his car and Ann walked alongside Reza to theirs. Once in the car, Reza smiled at Ann saying 'And there's me thinking Ruth was the sensible one.'

Chapter 13
The Fallout

For Ruth the next few months were, shall we say, complicated. Who knew that one simple error could cause so many problems. As Hussain had pointed out there were issues with Jay's school, because technically he wasn't in the country. It was also the school where Ruth taught, meaning double trouble, as she was, and yet wasn't, in the country. Passports, visas, and the paperwork Hussain had given Ruth, had to be deposited at both the Emirate authorities and then at the British Embassy for examination. Explanations were greeted with incredulity, disbelief, and very often with amusement.

After almost six months of wrangling with the various authorities, Ruth finally managed to bring everything back to the status quo, right in time for the summer break.

Sitting in their garden the weekend after schools had broken up, Ruth turned to her husband. 'Darling,' she said, 'Abi, Ann, and I were thinking of taking the kids away for a few weeks, maybe at the end of the month. We thought France might be nice this time of year. What do you think?'

'I think if you are going anywhere, you are going with me this time and I'll look after all the paperwork.' Toufiq's tone left no room for argument.

It did get better, but it was quite a while before Ruth could be trusted to travel solo again.

Chapter 14
The Return

Two years later Ann and Reza were discussing their summer plans, they couldn't quite decide whether to stay in the Emirates, where they were guaranteed wall-to-wall sunshine, but with excessive heat and probably high humidity for most of the summer months, or whether to go further afield.

'I haven't seen my family for a while now,' said Reza ' so how do you feel about Turkey this year?'

Ann glanced sideways to see whether he was joking but he appeared to be quite serious. 'I'm not sure I would feel too comfortable after what happened last time.'

'But it would be different this time, there will only be the two of us and we're not likely to end up in that situation, not with the way you check and double-check everything.'

'That's true. What exactly do you have in mind?'

'I thought we could go via Istanbul, stay there for a week or so, and do a bit of sightseeing. Go to places you didn't manage last time and there are some even I haven't seen.'

'Like where, specifically?'

'I don't know, but off the top of my head there's the Basilica Cistern, that's supposed to be quite special. It's an underground sort of palace-type thing. Then there's the hippodrome and a couple of museums, one of archaeology and another of Turkish and Islamic art. There's the Dolmabahçe Palace and we could do the Galata Tower, there's a great restaurant at the top of that. We could even do the Bosphorous Cruise, that's an all-day thing.'

'That all sounds great but what about your family?'

'We don't have to be too set on timings. I could just tell them we're coming, give them a rough date and say we'll let them know nearer the time. That way we can stay in Istanbul for as long as we want and then head down to the family when we're ready. Come on… let's do it. There's nothing to stop us.'

Ann remained cautious but the sound of all those amazing places was really too good to pass up. 'Okay. Let's do it.'

The next day they visited the travel agents and booked their flights and as Ann had been so impressed with the Hotel Ayrias, its central location for all the sights and ease of getting around, they decided to book there for their stay in Istanbul.

A week later they arrived in Istanbul, without encountering any problems on the journey, much to

Ann's relief. They were soon in a taxi and on their way to Fatih district and the hotel Ayrias.

It looked exactly the same as Ann remembered it, except of course it was now summer, it was warm and the sun was shining brightly.

Entering the hotel, Ann felt immediately at home and much more relaxed than she had when she'd arrived two years before. She was, however, amazed to find Miray was still working behind the reception desk.

Reza handed over their passports to her for check-in and Miray glanced at them and confirmed the register for their booking. As she handed them back to Reza she looked up and saw Ann. 'Madam! Welcome back. I remember you. You were the English ladies, no passport. Yes?'

Ann wanted the ground to open up and swallow her…

Follow Maisie Sullivan:

https://maisiesullivanauthor.com

https://www.facebook.com/MaisiePaperbackWriter52

https://www.instagram.com/maisiesullivanauthor

maisiesullivanauthor@gmail.com

Five Days in Istanbul

Printed in Great Britain
by Amazon